ROBIN HOOD'S

BRIDGE MEMOIRS

ROBIN HOOD'S

BRIDGE MEMOIRS

David Bird

First published in the United Kingdom in 1997 by B. T. Batsford.

This edition published in 2013 by
Mr Bridge
Ryden Grange
Knaphill
Surrey
GU21 2TH

Copyright © **Mr Bridge**
Text © David Bird 1997

The moral right of the author has been asserted.

ISBN 1-85665-036-7

A CIP catalogue record for this book is available from the British Library.

Typeset by Ruth Edmondson, Saltash, Cornwall
Printed by The Magazine Printing Company, Brimsdown, Middlesex

CONTENTS

1	Christmas Eve at the Drunken Partridge	7
2	A Winter's Afternoon	19
3	Sunday in Sherwood	29
4	Friar Tuck's Invitation	41
5	The Royal Visitor	57
6	The Five Angels Tavern	71
7	The Michaelmas Individual	81
8	The Lucas Street Pairs	97
9	The One-Eyed Man	111
10	The St Bonaventure Chalice	125
11	Shoot-Out at Table One	137

1
CHRISTMAS EVE AT THE DRUNKEN PARTRIDGE

For as long as anyone could remember, a Christmas Eve pairs championship had been held at the Drunken Partridge alehouse. No entry fees were charged but each contestant was expected to contribute to the prize list. Henry Burthorpe, the baker from Wykham Village, had brought along a dozen of his best malted loaves. The outlaws had mainly given stolen trinkets or joints of venison.

Robin Hood and Maid Marian faced unknown opposition in the first round, two elderly nuns from the order of Saint Agnes the Destitute. 'Good evening, Sisters,' said Robin Hood, taking his seat. 'I trust the landlord showed due consideration and did not expect you to donate a prize.'

'We expect no special privileges,' declared Sister Beatrice.

'But, er ... I thought your order took a vow against possessions of any sort,' said Robin Hood.

Sister Percival assumed a beatific smile. 'Sister Beatrice and I prayed solidly for five hours that the winners of our prize should enjoy good health and a very long life,' she replied.

'A valuable prize indeed,' observed Robin Hood, reaching for his cards. This was the hand that met his eyes:

♠ A K Q 7 4
♡ K 6
♢ A K 6 4
♣ Q 7

It was perfect for the strong opening in the Nottingham Club system. 'One Club,' he said.

Maid Marian made the game-forcing response of 1NT, showing a balanced hand of 8-10 points. 'Two Spades,' said Robin Hood.

He stole a glance at Marian, who was contemplating her next move. Could there possibly be a more beautiful maiden in the whole of England? She hadn't much idea about bridge, it was true. But in a way such innocence added to her attraction.

'Four No-trumps?' said Maid Marian.

Sister Percival peered at Robin Hood. 'The Duke of Richmond's ace-ask?' she enquired.

'One and the same,' replied a good-humoured Robin Hood. How Marian had found such a call on a flat 8-10 hand was another matter. Still, on his present hand there was no reason not to make the correct response. 'Five Hearts,' he said.

'Five No-trumps?' said Maid Marian.

There was a limit to Robin Hood's indulgence. Since he had no intention of playing in a grand slam, good as his hand was, he decided to hide two of his kings. 'Six Diamonds,' he said.

With a look of disappointment Marian signed off in Six Spades. This was the full deal:

Game All. Dealer South.

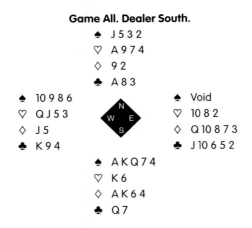

	♠	J 5 3 2
	♡	A 9 7 4
	◊	9 2
	♣	A 8 3

♠ 10 9 8 6	♠ Void
♡ Q J 5 3	♡ 10 8 2
◊ J 5	◊ Q 10 8 7 3
♣ K 9 4	♣ J 10 6 5 2

	♠	A K Q 7 4
	♡	K 6
	◊	A K 6 4
	♣	Q 7

West	North	East	South
Sister	*Maid*	*Sister*	*Robin*
Beatrice	*Marian*	*Percival*	*Hood*
			1♣
Pass	1NT	Pass	2♠
Pass	4NT	Pass	5♡
Pass	5NT	Pass	6◊
Pass	6♠	All Pass	

Sister Beatrice led the 10 of trumps, East showing out and Robin Hood winning with the ace. He paused to consider his line of play. All would be well if he could ruff one diamond low. The remaining diamond loser could then be ruffed low, or overruffed with the jack. Either way, he would be able to pick up West's trumps without loss, making the contract easily.

Robin Hood cashed the ace and king of diamonds and led a third round of the suit. Sister Beatrice defended well by ruffing with the 6, overruffed with the jack in dummy. It was time for a change of plan. Hood cashed the king and ace of hearts and ruffed a heart in his hand, both defenders following. He then cashed one more round of trumps to leave these cards outstanding:

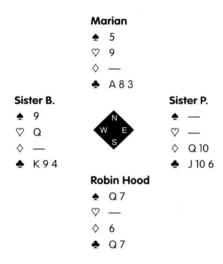

Marian
♠ 5
♡ 9
♢ —
♣ A 8 3

Sister B.
♠ 9
♡ Q
♢ —
♣ K 9 4

Sister P.
♠ —
♡ —
♢ Q 10
♣ J 10 6

Robin Hood
♠ Q 7
♡ —
♢ 6
♣ Q 7

When the last diamond was led Sister Beatrice had no good card to play. If she ruffed with the 9 declarer would throw dummy's last heart, leaving West endplayed. If, instead, she threw the heart queen, declarer would ruff and lead the established nine of hearts, throwing his club loser.

Sister Beatrice decided to throw a small club. Hood ruffed the diamond in dummy and was now able to return to hand by ruffing a heart low. He then drew the last trump, eventually conceding a trick to the king of clubs.

Sister Beatrice sucked in air between her few remaining teeth. 'Very aggravating end position, Sister,' she declared. 'A bottom for us, you can be sure of it.'

A few rounds later Robin and Marian faced a new partnership between Much, the Miller's son, and Will Scarlet. Rebellious by nature, Scarlet was always determined to outwit the outlaw leader at the card table. This was the first hand they played:

East/West Game. Dealer South.

```
                    ♠ K 2
                    ♡ A K Q 4 3
                    ◊ 7 3
                    ♣ Q J 6 2
   ♠ J 10 9 7 5 4 3          ♠ Q
   ♡ 8 7 6 2          N      ♡ J 10 9 5
   ◊ 10 8          W     E   ◊ A J 9 4
   ♣ Void             S      ♣ K 9 7 4
                    ♠ A 8 6
                    ♡ Void
                    ◊ K Q 6 5 2
                    ♣ A 10 8 5 3
```

West	North	East	South
Will	*Maid*	*Much*	*Robin*
Scarlet	*Marian*		*Hood*
			1◊
3♠	4♡	Pass	5♣
Pass	6♣	Dble	All Pass

Undeterred by the adverse vulnerability, Will Scarlet entered the auction with an overcall of Three Spades. Marian bid Four Hearts and Much gave some consideration to doubling this, or so it seemed to Robin Hood in the South seat. Realising it was not a particularly sound bid, he continued to Five Clubs. Marian bid a sixth club and it was no surprise when the Miller's son doubled this contract. The spade jack was led and down went the dummy.

'A fine hand for you, as you see,' declared Maid Marian.

Robin was surprised to find that, just for once, Marian actually did have a good hand. He won the spade lead with dummy's king and called for the queen of trumps. He ran this card successfully, West showing out. A diamond to the king followed and the key stage of the hand had been reached. A low diamond from declarer would be fatal; West would win with the 10 and give his partner a spade ruff. Appreciating this, Hood's next play was the queen of diamonds from his hand. East won with the ace and returned the jack of hearts. Hood discarded a spade from his hand and won in the dummy. A finesse of the 8 of trumps was followed by a diamond ruff. He then discarded his last two diamonds on the king and queen of hearts. It remained only to draw trumps and he had twelve tricks before him.

'Why did you double the slam, you great berk?' cried Will Scarlet. 'My Three Spades was weak, didn't you realise that?'

Much stared back nervously. 'Didn't look like none of 'is suits was breakin', Will,' he replied. 'Anyroad, I 'ad near an openin' bid myself. Why should they make a slam?'

Seeking support, Much turned towards the outlaw leader. 'Will should 'ave more than one jack for a Three Spade bid,' he said. 'Ain't that so, Robin?'

'It was certainly a brave call,' replied Robin Hood. 'Against a lesser bidder than Marian, it might have kept us out of the slam.'

'When Much doubled Six Clubs, I very nearly redoubled,' declared Marian, looking up from the travelling scoresheet. 'Not that it would have given us any more matchpoints, as it happens.'

On the next round, Robin and Marian faced Albert Gorse, landlord of the Drunken Partridge. His wife had her arm in a sling, after an unfortunate accident with a beer barrel, and he was partnered on this occasion by one of his barmaids. To ensure nothing untoward happened, the ample Mrs Gorse was sitting at the table, watching the game.

North/South Game. Dealer West.

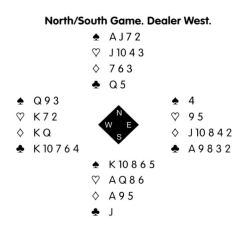

```
              ♠ A J 7 2
              ♡ J 10 4 3
              ◊ 7 6 3
              ♣ Q 5
  ♠ Q 9 3                    ♠ 4
  ♡ K 7 2          N         ♡ 9 5
  ◊ K Q         W     E      ◊ J 10 8 4 2
  ♣ K 10 7 6 4     S         ♣ A 9 8 3 2
              ♠ K 10 8 6 5
              ♡ A Q 8 6
              ◊ A 9 5
              ♣ J
```

West	North	East	South
Lizzie	Maid	Albert	Robin
	Marian	Gorse	Hood
1NT	Pass	2◊	Dble
Pass	3◊	Pass	3♡
Pass	4♡	All Pass	

The young barmaid, whose good looks were much admired by the Drunken Partridge clientele, placed the king of diamonds on the table.

'Eight fine points for you, Robin,' declared Maid Marian, as she displayed the dummy. 'Holding both majors, I had to force to game opposite your strong double.'

'Er ... yes, very well bid, my love,' replied Robin Hood. For the moment, however, it was not at all clear how ten tricks might be landed. He could hold up the ace of diamonds for one round, breaking the defenders' link in that suit. West would surely hold the trump king, though, and when she came on lead she would be able to cross in clubs for the setting trick in diamonds to be cashed. East must have one of the club honours, otherwise West would no doubt have led the suit. What could be done? Perhaps West held king-queen doubleton of diamonds. Ah yes, then the suit could be blocked.

Robin Hood decided to win the first round of diamonds. At trick two he made an important move – he led the jack of clubs, to kill the connection between the defenders' hands. West won with the king, cashed the queen of diamonds, and played another club, ruffed by declarer. West was known to hold the trump king, so Robin Hood continued with the ace and queen of trumps. An eventual finesse against the queen brought in the spade suit. Dummy's last diamond was discarded on declarer's long spade and ten tricks were there.

'What was you thinkin' of, Albert Gorse?' cried Mrs Gorse, from her seat just behind him.

Gorse, a good-natured man, turned round. 'What do you mean, my dear?' he said.

'Five-five shape at favourable vulnerability?' continued his wife. 'You must be mad not to sacrifice. Five Clubs only goes one down.'

'Very good point, my dear,' replied the landlord. 'I don't know how I missed the call.'

'Don't think much of their biddin', neither,' observed Mrs Gorse, rubbing her injured arm. 'Five-four fit in spades, they 'ad. Never mentioned the suit!'

Maid Marian inspected the scoresheet. 'Three pairs have played in spades so far,' she said. 'It seems they all made only nine tricks.'

'How strange,' said an amused Robin Hood. 'Just as well we mis-bid the hand, as it turned out. Playing in hearts, the spade suit provided a useful discard.'

A round or two later, Robin Hood and Marian faced the strong partnership of Friar Tuck and Nazir the Saracen. The Friar reached a slam on this deal:

East/West Game. Dealer North.

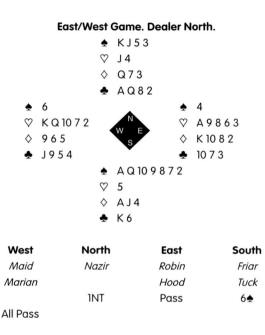

♠	K J 5 3	
♡	J 4	
♢	Q 7 3	
♣	A Q 8 2	

♠ 6
♡ K Q 10 7 2
♢ 9 6 5
♣ J 9 5 4

♠ 4
♡ A 9 8 6 3
♢ K 10 8 2
♣ 10 7 3

♠ A Q 10 9 8 7 2
♡ 5
♢ A J 4
♣ K 6

West	North	East	South
Maid	*Nazir*	*Robin*	*Friar*
Marian		*Hood*	*Tuck*
	1NT	Pass	6♠
All Pass			

At the dinner table it was Friars Tuck's custom to race through any *hors d'oeuvres,* the quicker to reach the more enjoyable main course. He followed a similar strategy at the bridge table, dispensing with the bidding as swiftly as possible. He leapt to Six Spades on the first round and Marian opened the defence with the king and queen of hearts.

Friar Tuck ruffed the second heart, drew the outstanding trumps in one round, and paused to consider his prospects. There seemed to be two roughly 50% lines available. He could take a straightforward finesse in diamonds. Alternatively, he could cash the ace of diamonds and run the trump suit. An automatic squeeze would develop if either defender held the king of diamonds and the club guard.

Friar Tuck was very much someone who liked to 'have his cake and eat it'. Surely the best line was to cross to dummy and lead the diamond queen. If East failed to cover with the king, he could overtake with the ace and play for the minor-suit squeeze.

Following this plan, the Friar crossed to dummy with a trump and called for the queen of diamonds. Hood produced a smooth 2 and Tuck overtook with the ace. Muttering a small prayer, he now ran the trump suit.

His prayer failed to reach its destination. Marian held on to all her clubs and the slam went one down.

'I don't believe it!' exclaimed Friar Tuck, when the lie of the cards became apparent. 'How could you possibly tell not to cover the queen of diamonds, Robin?'

'Not too difficult,' Robin Hood replied. 'I could place you with the king of clubs. Three club tricks, seven spades, and the diamond ace would bring your total to eleven. And you would hardly lead the queen of diamonds unless you held the jack; you'd be giving up the genuine chance of a squeeze against West.'

'Allah himself could not reason more soundly,' declared Nazir, giving his leader a congratulatory slap on the shoulder. His dark eyes narrowed as he inspected the scoresheet. 'Unfortunately, Tuck, everyone else seems to have made twelve tricks on our cards.'

'Doesn't surprise me one jot,' replied the Friar sourly. 'Most of this crowd would think the diamond finesse was the only chance.'

Robin Hood and Marian continued to do well. On the last round of the event they faced Little John and his straw-haired sweetheart, Meg.

'Young Meg looks an absolute delight,' exclaimed Hood. 'You're a lucky man, John.'

'It's true,' replied Little John, gazing proudly across the table. 'Mind you, so's the saying: *Lucky in Love, Unlucky in Cards.* We've 'ad terrible luck all evening.'

Yes, thought Robin Hood. Players of Little John's standard usually did suffer from bad luck.

Marian took a fair score in Four Spades on the first board, then Little John picked up these cards:

> ♠ K J 9 3
> ♡ K Q 8
> ◇ Q J 9
> ♣ J 5 4

'One Spade,' said Robin Hood, to his right.

Thirteen points sitting over the opening bid were worth more like sixteen, thought Little John. Against anyone else he would have overcalled 1NT. Still, best to hold back against Robin. 'No bid,' said Little John.

Maid Marian responded Two Clubs and raised Hood's rebid of Two

Hearts to Four Hearts. Little John's fingers moved towards the queen of diamonds. That was the best opening lead, surely. The auction was not yet over, however. 'Six Hearts,' said Robin Hood.

Little John inspected his cards once more. Robin wouldn't have bid the slam on a jack-high heart suit, surely? And if the ace of hearts sat to the right of his king-queen, only outright sorcery could stop him from making two trump tricks. 'Double,' said Little John.

There was no further bidding. Little John led the queen of diamonds and this proved to be the full deal:

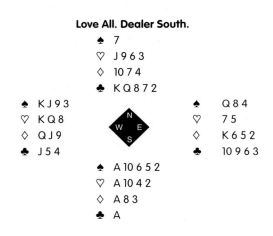

Love All. Dealer South.

```
                    ♠ 7
                    ♡ J 9 6 3
                    ◇ 10 7 4
                    ♣ K Q 8 7 2
    ♠ K J 9 3                        ♠ Q 8 4
    ♡ K Q 8          N               ♡ 7 5
    ◇ Q J 9      W       E           ◇ K 6 5 2
    ♣ J 5 4          S               ♣ 10 9 6 3
                    ♠ A 10 6 5 2
                    ♡ A 10 4 2
                    ◇ A 8 3
                    ♣ A
```

West	North	East	South
Little	Maid	Meg of	Robin
John	Marian	Wykham	Hood
			1♠
Pass	2♣	Pass	2♡
Pass	4♡	Pass	6♡
Dble	All Pass		

Robin Hood managed a glassy smile as he surveyed the dummy. 'Only six points for me, Marian?' he said. 'I was expecting rather more.'

'I could hardly raise to just Three Hearts with all this playing strength,' declared Maid Marian. 'Did you not notice my four fine trumps and the useful singleton in your main suit?'

Little John had a high opinion of Robin Hood's card-play and rarely doubled him for penalties. Hood could therefore be certain that both trump honours would lie offside. He won the diamond lead with the ace, cashed the ace of spades and ruffed a spade. A club to the ace allowed another spade to be ruffed and Hood continued with the king and queen of clubs, throwing his two diamond losers.

A diamond ruff in the South hand was followed by a fourth round of spades, ruffed with the 9. East was unable to overruff and Robin Hood ruffed dummy's last diamond. This end position had been reached:

Marian
♠ —
♡ J
♢ —
♣ 8 7

Little John
♠ —
♡ K Q 8
♢ —
♣ —

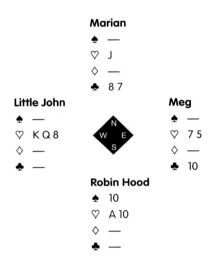

Meg
♠ —
♡ 7 5
♢ —
♣ 10

Robin Hood
♠ 10
♡ A 10
♢ —
♣ —

Little John scratched his head uncertainly as Robin Hood's last spade appeared on the table. He eventually ruffed with the king and returned the queen of trumps but Hood faced the ace and 10, claiming the last two tricks.

'There you are, Robin,' said Maid Marian. 'I thought you would make it.'

Meg gave Little John a sympathetic smile. 'You certainly 'ad your double on that one, love,' she said. 'Almost like magic the way 'e made twelve tricks.'

It was nearly midnight as the prize-giving began.

'In third place, winning two bushels of ripe pears,' announced the landlord, 'were John the Carter and his wife, Helen. Please step forward.'

'You'll 'ave to eat those, my dear,' laughed John the Carter. 'I can't abide the taste of pears.'

'And in second place, winning a barrel of my finest strong ale,' continued the Landlord, 'were Nazir the Saracen and our very own Friar Tuck.'

Nazir was also laughing as he strode forward. 'For me alcohol is forbidden,' he informed the applauding crowd. 'All praise be to Allah.'

'That doesn't cause any problem, as far as I can see,' declared Friar Tuck, taking gleeful charge of the barrel.

'And the first prize – a very special one – goes to the winners, Maid Marian and Robin Hood!' cried the landlord. 'Thanks to the virtuous Sisters of St Agnes here, our two winners will enjoy a long, happy and healthy life.'

Robin Hood put an arm around Marian as the two of them walked forward, 'I hope the good Lord is correctly informed of the result,' he said.

Marian gave Hood a playful pat on the cheek. 'Don't worry, Robin,' she said. 'I'll tell him myself when I say my prayers tonight.'

2
A WINTER'S AFTERNOON

It had been an unusually harsh winter and the wind was whistling through the arrow slits of Nottingham Castle. Inside the Sheriff's state-room it was warm, nevertheless, with a beechwood fire roaring in the grate.

Sir Guy of Gisburne, the tall blonde-haired commander of the Sheriff's men-at-arms, sorted through his cards. 'I shall open Three Hearts,' he said.

'No bid,' said the 20-year-old Anne of Carlyle.

Next to speak was the elegantly coiffeured Eleanor of Bayeux, a recently arrived visitor to the Castle. She gave a small sign. *'Je passe,'* she said.

The Sheriff of Nottingham, who had been gazing admiringly at the young beauty opposite, suddenly realised it was his turn to bid. He looked down at these cards:

♠ K Q 10 9 8 3
♡ 10 6 2
♦ A 4
♣ 7 4

Not much of a hand, it was true, but it could hardly be right to let Gisburne's pre-empt go unchallenged. 'Three Spades,' said the Sheriff.

After a pass by Gisburne, Anne of Carlyle seemed uncertain what to call. Eventually she raised to Four Spades and there was no further bidding.

This was the deal:

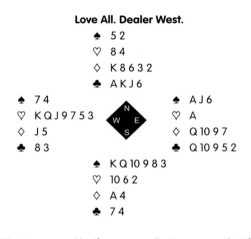

Love All. Dealer West.

```
                  ♠ 5 2
                  ♡ 8 4
                  ◇ K 8 6 3 2
                  ♣ A K J 6
    ♠ 7 4                           ♠ A J 6
    ♡ K Q J 9 7 5 3                 ♡ A
    ◇ J 5                           ◇ Q 10 9 7
    ♣ 8 3                           ♣ Q 10 9 5 2
                  ♠ K Q 10 9 8 3
                  ♡ 10 6 2
                  ◇ A 4
                  ♣ 7 4
```

West	North	East	South
Guy of Gisburne	*Anne of Carlyle*	*Lady Eleanor*	*The Sheriff*
3♡	Pass	Pass	3♠
Pass	4♠	All Pass	

Gisburne led the king of hearts and the pale-faced Anne laid out her dummy. 'I shouldn't really have raised with only two trumps, my Lord,' she said. 'I hope you will not be angry with me.'

The Sheriff directed a lustful glance at his slender-limbed partner. 'You bid it well, my dear,' he replied.

Eleanor of Bayeux looked on disapprovingly. Why, the man was incorrigible. It was disgraceful to shower such attention on a girl some thirty years younger than himself. She overtook the heart lead with the bare ace and switched to the ten of diamonds. After considering the matter for a few moments, the Sheriff won in the dummy. He finessed the 10 of trumps successfully and continued with the king of trumps, West following. Lady Eleanor won with the ace and returned a second round of diamonds to declarer's ace. The Sheriff drew the last trump, then crossed to dummy with the ace of clubs.

These cards were still out:

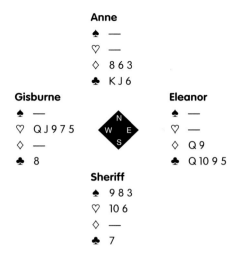

Anne
♠ —
♡ —
◇ 8 6 3
♣ K J 6

Gisburne
♠ —
♡ Q J 9 7 5
◇ —
♣ 8

Eleanor
♠ —
♡ —
◇ Q 9
♣ Q 10 9 5

Sheriff
♠ 9 8 3
♡ 10 6
◇ —
♣ 7

The Sheriff now led a diamond from dummy, the 9 appearing from East. If the diamonds were 3-3, the winning play would be to ruff the trick. Still, thought the Sheriff, in that case Gisburne would have started with 2-7-3-1 distribution. From such a hand he might have led the singleton club.

Concluding that East had started with four diamonds, the Sheriff discarded a heart on the third round of the suit. West showed out and Eleanor of Bayeux was left on lead. She surveyed her remaining cards, looking decidedly unhappy with the situation.

'It makes no difference what you play,' declared the Sheriff masterfully. 'A club will run into dummy's tenace. If you play a diamond instead, I can ruff and dummy's last diamond is good for a discard.'

'A fine piece of dummy play, my Lord,' declared Anne of Carlyle.

The Sheriff nodded. 'We were lucky that Gisburne opened just Three Hearts,' he observed. 'A full-blooded opening of Four Hearts would have shut us out of the auction.'

'But, my Lord,' protested Gisburne, 'I had three losing doubletons outside the long suit. Three Hearts was the perfect bid.'

'Three Hearts was the woman's bid on the hand,' declared the Sheriff scornfully. 'If any member of my yeomanry made such a call, I'd have him assigned to the kitchens immediately.'

Eleanor of Bayeux was aghast at this. 'A woman's bid, zat is unforgivable remark!' she exclaimed. 'In years to come it will be against ze Law to make such sexy comments.'

'If it is ever against the Law to state the blindingly obvious,' retorted the

Sheriff, 'I'll be all the more glad I was born in these sensible times.'

A hand or two later, with the score at Game All, the Sheriff picked up these cards:

♠ Q 9 8 5 3
♥ Q J 6 2
♦ 4
♣ 9 8 5

'Two Diamonds,' said the fair Anne.

This was the strongest opening in the Nottingham Club system, indicating upwards of 22 points. The Sheriff made the negative response of Two Hearts and Anne rebid Three Clubs. 'Three Spades,' said the Sheriff.

This bid seemed to cause something of a problem opposite. 'I never know how high to go on these hands, my Lord,' said Anne. 'You must tell me if I have been too cautious. Four Spades.'

A pronounced sense of ethics was not one of the requirements to rise to the office of Lord High Sheriff. 'Five Spades,' said the Sheriff.

Anne brightened. 'I was hoping you would bid again, my Lord,' she said. 'Six Spades.'

There was no further bidding. Gisburne led the kind of diamonds and this proved to be the full deal:

Game All. Dealer North.

```
              ♠  A K 6
              ♡  A K
              ◇  A 7 5
              ♣  A K 7 6 2
♠  J 10 4 2                      ♠  7
♡  10 8 7 3          N           ♡  9 5 4
◇  K Q 10 8 3    W     E         ◇  J 9 6 2
♣  Void             S           ♣  Q J 10 4 3
              ♠  Q 9 8 5 3
              ♡  Q J 6 2
              ◇  4
              ♣  9 8 5
```

West	North	East	South
Guy of	*Anne of*	*Lady*	*The*
Gisburne	*Carlyle*	*Eleanor*	*Sheriff*
	2◇	Pass	2♡
Pass	3♣	Pass	3♠
Pass	4♠	Pass	5♠
Pass	6♠	All Pass	

The Sheriff won the diamond lead with dummy's ace and cashed the ace and king of trumps, not pleased to see East show out on the second round. In addition to the unfortunate trump loser he seemed to have a certain loser in the club suit. Was there anything that could be done?

The Sheriff cashed the ace and king of hearts, then ruffed a diamond in the South hand. Gisburne followed to the next two rounds of hearts and two clubs were thrown from the dummy. The Sheriff then led a low club. It would not help Gisburne to ruff a loser with a certain trump trick. He discarded a diamond and dummy's club ace won the trick. The Sheriff ruffed dummy's last diamond in his hand and surveyed this end position:

Anne
- ♠ 6
- ♡ —
- ◇ —
- ♣ K 7

Gisburne
- ♠ J 10
- ♡ —
- ◇ Q
- ♣ —

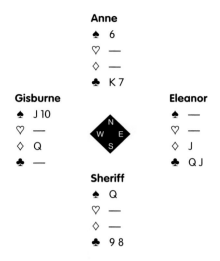

Eleanor
- ♠ —
- ♡ —
- ◇ J
- ♣ Q J

Sheriff
- ♠ Q
- ♡ —
- ◇ —
- ♣ 9 8

When the Sheriff led another club towards the dummy Gisburne had no answer. If he discarded, dummy's king of clubs would score and declarer's master trump would bring his total to twelve. Gisburne decided to ruff but, whether he played a trump or the diamond queen next, declarer had the last two tricks.

'It was lucky we played in spades and not clubs, my Lord,' observed Anne. 'Lady Eleanor held five clubs to the queen-jack-ten.'

Lady Eleanor of Bayeux nodded her coiffeured head. *'Mais oui,'* she said. 'If you are bidding Six Clubs I would 'ave a very safe double.'

Gisburne raised his eyes to the ceiling. Fancy having to partner someone who would happily drive the opponents from a failing slam into a making slam. These games were always a pain in the backside.

'The rubber comes to 17 shillings,' declared the Sheriff. He looked lecherously across the table. 'You are in fine form today, Anne.'

Anne of Carlyle inclined her head shyly. 'If you say so, my Lord,' she replied.

By the time the third rubber started, the winter sun was no longer visible through the arrow slits. It was by the light of the wall braziers that the Sheriff inspected this hand:

♠ A Q J 10 9 5
♡ 5
♦ K Q 8 2
♣ A 4

He opened with a strong Nottingham club and Anne made the negative response of One Diamond, denying 8 points. The Sheriff rebid One Spade and Anne bid Two Hearts. He continued with Two Spades and Anne bid Three Hearts. The Sheriff stole a glance at the young beauty opposite him. Fair of skin she may be, but she had little idea how to play the cards.

'Three Spades,' he said.

'Four Hearts,' said Anne, after a short pause.

'Double!' said Lady Eleanor.

The Sheriff bid a resolute Four Spades and was relieved to find the call passed out. This was the full deal:

Love All. Dealer South.

```
              ♠ 3 2
              ♡ J 9 7 6 4 2
              ♦ A 3
              ♣ 8 7 3
♠ K 6                         ♠ 8 7 4
♡ 8 3            N            ♡ A K Q 10
♦ J 7 5 4    W     E          ♦ 10 9 6
♣ Q J 10 9 5     S            ♣ K 6 2
              ♠ A Q J 10 9 5
              ♡ 5
              ♦ K Q 8 2
              ♣ A 4
```

West	North	East	South
Guy of	*Anne of*	*Lady*	*The*
Gisburne	*Carlyle*	*Eleanor*	*Sheriff*
			1♣
Pass	1♦	Pass	1♠
Pass	2♡	Pass	2♠
Pass	3♡	Pass	3♠
Pass	4♡	Dble	4♠
All Pass			

Gisburne led the queen of clubs and down went the dummy. Good grief, thought the Sheriff. How could anyone be so stupid as to bid a suit of six to the jack three times?

'Did my bidding please you, my Lord?' asked Anne.

The Sheriff managed a small nod, then turned his mind to the play. There was a possible loser in each suit but it seemed that the diamond loser might be ruffed in the dummy. What if he won the club lead, played the ace and king of diamonds, and ruffed a diamond? If a trump finesse were then to lose, the defenders might manoeuvre a ruff of the diamond queen. He could reduce their communications by ducking this first club, and maybe then conceding a heart trick, but the line would still be far from safe.

'May I play a card from dummy for you, my Lord?' enquired Anne sweetly.

Had anyone else dared to interrupt his train of thought, the Sheriff would have reacted strongly. 'In a moment, Anne,' he replied.

Spotting a better line, the Sheriff won the first round of clubs with the ace and played the three top diamonds, throwing a club from the dummy. He then led a fourth round of diamonds, discarding dummy's last club. After these preliminaries the Sheriff could not be prevented from ruffing a club in dummy. Five trumps, four minor-suit winners, and a club ruff brought his total to ten tricks.

'At least no-one can complain about my bidding,' declared Eleanor of Bayeux. 'Ze double of Four 'earts was very sound. It would 'ave gone three down, I think.'

This was too much for Gisburne. 'Wouldn't three down, even undoubled, have been just a tiny bit better than them making Four Spades?' he enquired.

Lady Eleanor's mouth dropped. She turned towards the Sheriff. 'Ow can you let 'im speak to me like zat?' she demanded. 'I am your guest in ze Castle. Was I invited 'ere to be insulted by some uncultivated juvenile?'

'Hardly a juvenile, Eleanor,' retorted the Sheriff. 'His innocent looks belie his age, I believe. How old are you, Gisburne?'

'Thirty-one, my Lord,' replied Gisburne sullenly.

The Frenchwoman glared at her partner. 'At least one year of so many should have been spent to learn some manners,' she informed him.

On the next hand the Sheriff reached a slam.

North/South Game. Dealer West.

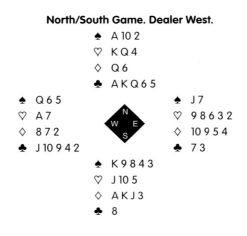

```
                    ♠ A 10 2
                    ♡ K Q 4
                    ◇ Q 6
                    ♣ A K Q 6 5
    ♠ Q 6 5                            ♠ J 7
    ♡ A 7                              ♡ 9 8 6 3 2
    ◇ 8 7 2                            ◇ 10 9 5 4
    ♣ J 10 9 4 2                       ♣ 7 3
                    ♠ K 9 8 4 3
                    ♡ J 10 5
                    ◇ A K J 3
                    ♣ 8
```

West	North	East	South
Guy of	*Anne of*	*Lady*	*The*
Gisburne	*Carlyle*	*Eleanor*	*Sheriff*
Pass	2NT	Pass	3♠
Pass	4♠	Pass	6♠
All Pass			

Gisburne led the jack of clubs and the Sheriff surveyed the dummy with mixed feelings. At least he had been spared a heart lead. If clubs were 4-3 he might be able to set up a long club and discard all three hearts before the defenders gained the lead with their master trump. He won with the ace of clubs and continued with the king of clubs, throwing a heart. He next led dummy's queen of clubs.

Lady Eleanor turned triumphantly towards the Sheriff. 'Bad news for you, my Lord,' she said, ruffing with seven of spades.

Not necessarily, thought the Sheriff as he overruffed with the 8. If the ruff was from a 3-card holding he would now make the contract; he could draw the outstanding trumps in two rounds, then concede just one trick in hearts. He cashed the king of trumps, noting with interest the appearance of the jack from East.

The Sheriff sat back in his tapestry-covered chair. Should he finesse in trumps or play for the drop? It wasn't a close decision, surely. Eleanor would not have looked so pleased with herself if she was ruffing from Q-J-x – a natural trump trick. Nor, moderate player that she was, would she have ruffed low from such a holding. With some confidence the Sheriff played a trump to the 10. When a heart discard came from East, he was able to claim twelve tricks.

Gisburne could take no more. 'Why did you ruff the club, woman?' he demanded. 'He can't discard all his hearts. So long as you don't ruff, we must score a trump and the ace of hearts.'

Eleanor of Bayeux's eyes grew to twice their normal size. 'You had an ace and you did not lead it against a slam?' she cried. 'Are you mad?'

It was all the Sheriff could do to restrain himself from laughing openly 'Yes, you must cash the ace, Gisburne,' he said. 'Then it will be clear to Lady Eleanor not to ruff in. The Q-x-x opposite J-x in trumps combine to make a certain second trick. Do you see?'

'But, my Lord, only last week I cashed such an ace against a slam,' said Gisburne. 'Declarer then played me for the queen of trumps and you were furious. You said I'd given away the position of the queen by making such a lead.'

'It was an entirely different situation,' declared the Sheriff. 'I'm so sorry, Eleanor. I'll get someone stronger next time.'

A disgruntled Eleanor of Bayeux rose to her feet. 'A weak player opposite, I do not mind,' she said. 'One with no manners who blames his own mistakes on *la pauvre partenaire,* zat I do not like'

The players settled up for the final rubber and Sir Guy of Gisburne then left to escort the Frenchwoman back to her guest room.

The Sheriff eyed the young Anne lasciviously. 'Now, Anne,' he said. 'No need for you to leave. I have a Spanish wine that may interest you.'

'My Lord,' replied Anne, 'would it not be rather improper without a chaperone present?'

'With an untrustworthy fellow such as Gisburne, so it would,' replied the Sheriff, closing the door. 'But I am a lifelong friend of your family.'

'Surely, my Lord, we should leave the door open?' persisted Anne.

'No need for that, my dear,' declared the Sheriff, turning the key in the lock. 'Now, where did I put that bottle of wine? They tell me that 1087 was a very fine vintage.'

3
SUNDAY IN SHERWOOD

Robin Hood was not a particularly religious man. Even so, he held that there should be no violence on the Lord's Day. No raids were perpetrated, nor any hold-ups. Even archery practice was prohibited. The outlaws were expected to attend Friar Tuck's service at 11 o'clock and this was followed by a traditional Sunday lunch of venison or wild boar.

In the afternoon the outlaws passed the time by playing bridge. On the present occasion six or seven outlaws were watching the game in which Robin Hood was playing.

'Gluttony's a sin, isn't it, Tuck?' said Little John, dealing the cards for the next hand. 'You must 'ave come precious close to it at lunch. Didn't I see you goin' back twice for more meat?'

'Very modest portions all three of them,' retorted the Friar. 'It is only fair to show appreciation of those who have laboured over the roasting.'

'Thoughtful as ever,' said Maid Marian, giving Friar Tuck a playful dig in the ribs.

The players picked up their cards for the following deal:

Game All. Dealer West.

```
              ♠ Q 9 5
              ♡ A J 5 3
              ◇ A 10 5
              ♣ Q J 3
♠ A 10 8 7 4              ♠ 6 3 2
♡ K 9 7        N         ♡ 10 8 4
◇ K 8       W   E        ◇ Q 9 3
♣ A 10 4       S         ♣ K 8 5 2
              ♠ K J
              ♡ Q 6 2
              ◇ J 7 6 4 2
              ♣ 9 7 6
```

West	North	East	South
Little	*Maid*	*Friar*	*Robin*
John	*Marian*	*Tuck*	*Hood*
1♠	Dble	Pass	1NT
Pass	2NT	Pass	3NT
All Pass			

Little John led the seven of spades against 3NT and Maid Marian displayed her dummy. 'Not the best of 16-point hands, I realise,' she said. 'I should have passed 1NT.'

'Not the best of 14-point hands, either,' observed Friar Tuck, chuckling to himself.

'Only 14, is it?' said Marian. 'Well, it will make no difference, the way Robin plays the cards.'

Robin Hood surveyed the limited assets before him. Could the situation be rectified? He won the spade lead with the jack and led a diamond to the 10. Friar Tuck would have done well to duck this, killing the entry to the long diamonds in the South hand. He won with the queen however, and returned a spade. Little John could see that there was no point in holding off the ace. Indeed, such a play would increase the chance of his being endplayed later in the hand. He won with the ace and cleared the spade suit.

In dummy with the spade queen, Hood cashed the ace of diamonds. His spirits rose when the king fell from West. Two more rounds of diamonds left this end position, with declarer needing four more tricks:

Marian
♠ —
♡ A J 5
♢ —
♣ Q J 3

Little John
♠ 10 8
♡ K 9 7
♢ —
♣ A

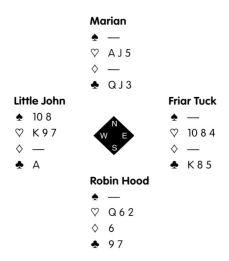

Friar Tuck
♠ —
♡ 10 8 4
♢ —
♣ K 8 5

Robin Hood
♠ —
♡ Q 6 2
♢ 6
♣ 9 7

To defend the position, Little John would have needed to keep ♡K-9-7 ♣A-10 as his last five cards. As it was, he had no good discard when the last diamond was played. If he threw a heart, declarer would score three tricks in the suit. If he threw the ace of clubs, declarer would take the heart finesse and establish a ninth trick in clubs. Little John decided to throw one of his spade winners, retaining a double guard on the heart king. Robin Hood threw the three of clubs from dummy, then finessed the jack of hearts successfully. A club to West's ace allowed him to cash one spade but he then had to lead away from the heart king. Against all initial expectations, declarer now had nine tricks.

'You see?' exclaimed a delighted Maid Marian. 'I thought I was worth my raise.'

'You judged it well,' said Robin Hood, maintaining a straight face. 'You had just the right cards for me.'

On the first hand of the next rubber Little John opened Three Diamonds. The next two players passed and Robin Hood had to find a call on this hand:

♠ A 6 4 2
♡ Q J 10 7 6
◇ J 4
♣ A K

The most flexible action was surely a double. Still, that would risk Marian becoming the declarer. 'Three Hearts,' said Robin Hood.

Maid Marian raised to the heart game and this turned out to be the full deal:

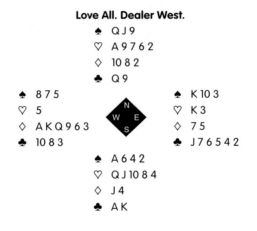

Love All. Dealer West.

West	North	East	South
Little	Maid	Friar	Robin
John	Marian	Tuck	Hood
3◇	Pass	Pass	3♡
Pass	4♡	All Pass	

Little John led the ace of diamonds and down went the dummy. 'With five-card trump support I was sorely tempted to bid a Richmond 4NT,' observed Maid Marian. 'I hope we haven't missed a slam.'

Robin Hood smiled at the suggestion. 'If you're not careful, Marian,' he said, 'you'll have these lads thinking you're an overbidder.'

At trick two Little John continued with the king of diamonds, Friar Tuck and Robin Hood looking surprised to see each other follow suit. 'A six-card pre-empt, John?' said Hood. 'That's unlike you.'

When Little John led the queen of diamonds to the next trick, Tuck discarded a club and Hood ruffed in the South hand. He then led the queen of trumps, West following with a small card. Little John would scarcely have pre-empted with 12 points, so the trump king was known to be offside. Hood overtook with the ace and a small card appeared from East. A simple endplay now beckoned. Hood cashed his two club winners and exited with a trump. Friar Tuck won with the bare king and had to open the spade suit or concede a ruff-and-discard. His spade exit ran to dummy's 9 and Hood now led the queen of spades, picking up East's king to land the game.

Friar Tuck shook his head. 'Unimaginative defence, partner,' he declared. 'It was obvious I would be endplayed. After cashing one diamond you should have switched to a spade.'

'Rubbish!' exclaimed Little John. 'If I don't cash the diamonds straight away I might never make them.'

'Suppose your spade switch goes to the queen, king and ace,' persisted Friar Tuck. 'Declarer cannot endplay me while I still have a diamond. And if he plays a diamond himself you can win and play a second spade, clearing my trick in the suit.'

'Double-dummy rubbish!' declared Little John, not happy to have his defence queried before so many onlookers. ''Ow could I tell you were goin' to be endplayed? I thought Robin 'ad the king of trumps.'

'Call it what you will,' declared the Friar. 'It's the only way to beat the contract.'

Robin Hood caught the Friar's eye. 'There was another way,' he said.

'Oh?' said Tuck. 'What was that?'

'If the impending endplay was so obvious, you might have ruffed John's queen of diamonds with the king,' replied Hood. 'That saves you from the endplay. I can discard one of my spades but I still have a spade loser.'

'Exactly!' roared Little John. He turned to the onlookers behind him. 'Typical priest, ain't he? Blamin' his own sins on the congregation.'

The rubber had advanced to Game All when this deal arose:

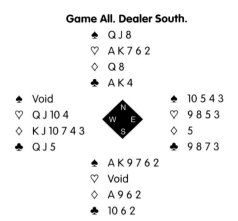

Game All. Dealer South.

                    ♠ Q J 8
                    ♡ A K 7 6 2
                    ◇ Q 8
                    ♣ A K 4

♠ Void   ♠ 10 5 4 3
♡ Q J 10 4   ♡ 9 8 5 3
◇ K J 10 7 4 3   ◇ 5
♣ Q J 5   ♣ 9 8 7 3

                    ♠ A K 9 7 6 2
                    ♡ Void
                    ◇ A 9 6 2
                    ♣ 10 6 2

West	North	East	South
Little	*Maid*	*Friar*	*Robin*
John	*Marian*	*Tuck*	*Hood*
			1♠
Pass	4NT	Pass	5♡
Pass	5NT	Pass	6◇
Pass	7♠	All Pass	

Little John led the queen of hearts against Seven Spades and Maid Marian laid out the dummy as if it were some rich string of pearls. 'Look what a fine hand I have for you,' she said.

'Very handsome,' agreed Hood. Now, how many top tricks did he have? Six trumps and five side-suit winners. Not bad, there would have been no problem in game.

Robin Hood won the heart lead and cashed a second heart, discarding two diamonds. A heart ruff was followed by a trump to the dummy, West showing out. When he ruffed a second heart both defenders followed. The long heart in dummy brought his potential total to twelve tricks, one short of the target. Robin Hood drew East's remaining trumps, then crossed to dummy with the club ace. These cards remained:

Marian
♠ —
♡ 7
♢ Q 8
♣ K

Little John
♠ —
♡ —
♢ K J
♣ Q J

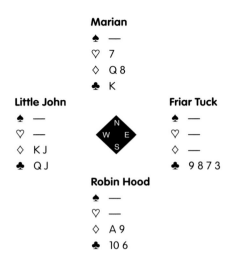

Friar Tuck
♠ —
♡ —
♢ —
♣ 9 8 7 3

Robin Hood
♠ —
♡ —
♢ A 9
♣ 10 6

Robin Hood played the long heart from dummy, discarding ♢9 from his hand. Little John had no good discard. When he threw the jack of clubs, Hood cashed the club king, dropping West's queen. He then returned to his hand with the ace of diamonds and scored the thirteenth trick with ♣10.

'Bravo, Robin!' cried Much the Miller's son, one of the spectators. 'I couldn't see 'ow you would do it.'

Hood smiled modestly. 'It was a fortunate lie of the cards,' he replied.

A disgruntled Friar Tuck extracted a leather purse from inside his cassock and counted out the coins owed for the rubber. 'I think I'll cut out,' he said. 'Rather too hot for me today.'

Alan A'Dale, an unusually good-looking man who had made a living as a minstrel before joining the outlaws, took the Friar's place.

This was the first hand of the new rubber.

Love All. Dealer East.

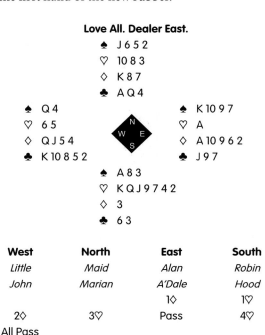

	♠	J 6 5 2
	♥	10 8 3
	♦	K 8 7
	♣	A Q 4

♠ Q 4   ♠ K 10 9 7
♥ 6 5   ♥ A
♦ Q J 5 4   ♦ A 10 9 6 2
♣ K 10 8 5 2   ♣ J 9 7

♠ A 8 3
♥ K Q J 9 7 4 2
♦ 3
♣ 6 3

West	North	East	South
Little	*Maid*	*Alan*	*Robin*
John	*Marian*	*A'Dale*	*Hood*
		1◇	1♡
2◇	3♡	Pass	4♡
All Pass			

The queen of diamonds was led and Marian laid out the dummy. 'Your overcall promised five hearts,' she observed, 'so I was happy to raise you with only three trumps.'

'I see,' replied Hood, 'but perhaps a raise to Two Hearts would have been enough. The king of diamonds isn't worth much under Alan's opening bid.'

'You're forgetting that in the Nottingham Club an opening of One Diamond may be prepared,' said Marian. 'I could hardly give you just a single raise, holding ten points.'

Robin Hood allowed West's queen of diamonds to win the first trick. He ruffed the diamond continuation and played a trump, won by East's ace. Hood ruffed the diamond ace return and cashed the ace of spades, drawing the 4, 2 and 7. He then took the club finesse, perking up somewhat when this succeeded. The club suit was eliminated, leaving these cards outstanding:

Marian
- ♠ J 6 5
- ♡ 8
- ♢ —
- ♣ —

Little John
- ♠ Q
- ♡ —
- ♢ 5
- ♣ K 10

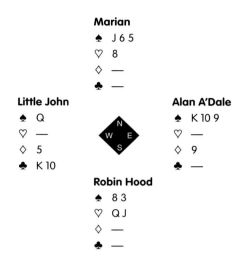

Alan A'Dale
- ♠ K 10 9
- ♡ —
- ♢ 9
- ♣ —

Robin Hood
- ♠ 8 3
- ♡ Q J
- ♢ —
- ♣ —

When a spade was played, Little John found himself on lead with the queen. Declarer's remaining spade loser went away on the ruff-and-discard return and the contract was made.

Alan A'Dale reached behind him for his lute and, to the great entertainment of the onlookers, burst into song:

> *An oversized fellow in Lincoln green-O,*
> *The worst defender you've ever seen-O,*
> *One day he forgot to unblock his queen-O,*
> *And Four Hearts was made-O!*

'You'll get my stave down yer throat if you don't shut up,' exclaimed Little John. 'What yer talkin' about, anyway?'

'When Robin played the ace of spades, you should have thrown your queen under it,' explained Alan A'Dale. 'Then I can win the next two spades with the king and 10.'

Little John's memory of the hand was fading rapidly. In any case, his analysis of a hand rarely extended beyond a single word. 'Rubbish!' he declared.

Not long afterwards Robin Hood was in game once again. This was the deal:

North/South Game. Dealer North.

```
              ♠ 6
              ♡ K 2
              ◊ A J 8 6 5 2
              ♣ A 8 7 3

   ♠ K J 9 7 5 2              ♠ Q 8 4
   ♡ 9 8 6 5         N        ♡ J 10 3
   ◊ Void         W     E     ◊ K Q 9 4
   ♣ 6 5 4           S        ♣ K J 2

              ♠ A 10 3
              ♡ A Q 7 4
              ◊ 10 7 3
              ♣ Q 10 9
```

West	North	East	South
Little	*Maid*	*Alan*	*Robin*
John	*Marian*	*A'Dale*	*Hood*
	1◊	Pass	1♡
Pass	2◊	Pass	3NT
All Pass			

Attaching some weight to his three tens, Robin Hood bid 3NT at his second turn. Little John attacked in spades and Hood held up the ace until the third round, discarding two clubs from the dummy. When he turned to the diamond suit, West showed out on the first round; dummy's jack lost to East's queen, and Alan A'Dale switched to the jack of hearts. Hood ran this to dummy's king and led a second round of diamonds towards the 10 in his hand. Alan A'Dale went in with the king and persisted with ♡10.

Declarer's problems were at an end. Hood won the second round of hearts with the ace, cashed the heart queen and ◊10, then crossed to dummy with the ace of clubs. The three remaining diamond winners brought his total to nine tricks.

Alan A'Dale shook his head. 'What's the point of clearing the spades, John?' he said. 'You didn't have an entry, did you? You should have switched to clubs.'

'Give us a song about it, Alan,' shouted one of the onlookers.

The minstrel played a few tuneful chords on his lute. Then, ignoring

Little John's black expression, burst into song:

> *After two spades, there came a small hitch-O,*
> *Blundering John couldn't find the club switch-O,*
> *Three No-trumps came home, making Robin Hood rich-O,*
> *All on a summer's day-O!*

'Right, you've asked for it,' declared Little John, reaching for his stave. 'That's absolute rubbish, that is.'

Robin Hood placed a restraining hand on Little John's arm. 'I fear John is right on this occasion,' he declared. 'You had a fine chance to beat 3NT yourself, Alan.'

The minstrel put down his lute. 'Oh?' he said.

'When you took your second diamond winner you could have returned the king of clubs,' said Robin Hood. 'That drives out the entry to dummy while the diamonds are still blocked. I can score three club tricks, finessing against the jack, but that still leaves me a trick short.'

'Exactly!' cried Little John. 'I'm partnerin' the village idiot today. Give me that lute, Alan, I'm goin' to sing a song.'

The onlookers winced as Little John strummed his introduction. It was rhythmical enough, in a strange way, but suffered from the fact that he could not form any chords with his left hand. The sound of the lute was soon drowned by Little John's voice:

> *A flatulent berk called Alan A'Dale-O,*
> *Never liked any opponent's contract to fail-O,*
> *Er ... when a bloody obvious king of clubs switch*
> *would have knocked out an entry-O,*
> *He played a heart and Robin got out of jail-O.*

There was prolonged cheering from the onlookers and several other outlaws emerged from the trees, wondering what was happening.

'Excellent, John!' declared Robin Hood, clapping his hands. 'But no second verse, please.'

4
FRIAR TUCK'S INVITATION

Friar Tuck surveyed the vellum scroll with some interest. 'The Deacon of Durham has died,' he said.

Hood looked up from a bow that he was re-stringing. 'Sad news,' he replied. 'Not that I have ever met the gentleman.'

'One of the richest clerics in the country,' continued Friar Tuck. 'His family has an estate of some 5,000 acres near the Scottish border.'

'Very pleasant for them,' observed Robin Hood, bending the bow to its full extent. 'Not much use to us, however.'

'It says here that the Deacon has left the sum of one thousand pounds to be donated to the poor,' said Friar Tuck. 'His will states that a bridge pairs competition should be held. The winners of the event may distribute the thousand pounds to the needy in their own region.'

'You are serious?' queried Robin Hood. 'Nazir and I would be very willing to play.'

'Don't be ridiculous,' replied Friar Tuck. 'The entry is restricted to the priesthood. Anyone looking less like a priest than Nazir, it is hard to imagine.'

'Then I will play with you,' declared Hood. 'I'm sure one of your cassocks will fit me, if we remove a few yards of cloth.'

A month or so later Robin Hood and Friar Tuck travelled to Durham. They were not alone in the pilgrimage. Some forty pairs had gathered in an attempt to win the large sum for their local poor.

The event was to be of 48 boards and in the first round the outlaw pair faced two Franciscan friars. Defying their advanced years, they had travelled from the extremes of Cornwall, a journey of some eleven days.

Love All. Dealer. South.

```
                    ♠ A 9 8
                    ♡ A K 9 5
                    ◇ A Q J 6 2
                    ♣ 8
    ♠ 10 7 5 4                      ♠ K J 6
    ♡ 8 7 4 3          N            ♡ Void
    ◇ Void          W     E         ◇ 10 9 8 5 4 3
    ♣ K 9 7 6 5        S            ♣ Q J 10 4
                    ♠ Q 3 2
                    ♡ Q J 10 6 2
                    ◇ K 7
                    ♣ A 3 2
```

West	North	East	South
Brother	*Friar*	*Brother*	*Robin*
Pierre	*Tuck*	*William*	*Hood*
			1♡
Pass	4NT	Pass	5◇
Pass	5♠	Pass	6◇
Pass	7♡	All Pass	

The white-haired Brother Pierre, who was looking distinctly the worse for wear after his long trek, leaned forward. 'Are you playing the Richmond 4NT?' he enquired. 'You know, that new bid which asks how many aces partner holds?'

Robin Hood peered back from under the cowl of his cassock. 'Actually, Brother, we are playing a new version of that convention,' he replied. 'Nottingham Key-Card Richmond.'

The elderly friar recoiled in his seat. 'I thought that only simple conventions were allowed in this event,' he declared.

'It is simple, Brother,' replied Robin Hood. 'My Five Diamonds showed one of the five aces. Five Spades asked if I held the trump queen and my Six Diamonds said that I did hold that card, and also the king of diamonds.'

'It seems we have wasted our time walking such a distance,' said Brother Pierre. 'We are facing a bunch of professionals here, Brother William. The poor of the Cornish fishing villages will have to go hungry.'

His partner, who had a walking stick propped up against his chair, nodded sympathetically. 'Your lead, Brother,' he said.

West led a trump, won by dummy's ace, and East showed out, throwing a diamond. Robin Hood observed this discard with some interest. With dummy's powerful diamonds on display East would scarcely throw a diamond from a 5-card holding. He might hold three or four small cards in the suit, but in that case he would doubtless have had an easy discard in one of the black suits. No, there was a distinct possibility that the man had started with all six of the missing diamonds.

Robin Hood crossed to the ace of clubs and ruffed a club. To ruff a second club would involve using the diamond king as an entry to the South hand at some stage. Fearing that West was void in the suit, Hood abandoned this idea. He cashed dummy's ace of spades and ran the trump suit. This end position resulted:

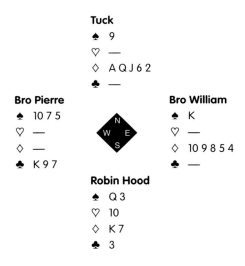

Tuck
♠ 9
♡ —
♢ A Q J 6 2
♣ —

Bro Pierre
♠ 10 7 5
♡ —
♢ —
♣ K 9 7

Bro William
♠ K
♡ —
♢ 10 9 8 5 4
♣ —

Robin Hood
♠ Q 3
♡ 10
♢ K 7
♣ 3

On the last trump declarer threw a spade from dummy. East was caught in a simple squeeze and had to concede a thirteenth trick.

'What a disappointment!' exclaimed Brother Pierre, sitting West. 'I had a void diamond, partner. I was hoping that declarer would run into a ruff, trying to cross to his king of diamonds.'

Friar Tuck nodded his congratulations. 'You read the cards well,' he declared.

'Not difficult,' replied Robin Hood. 'East's diamond discard might have been from three or four small, but in that case dummy's diamonds were all good. I would need only one club ruff anyway.'

A round or two later the outlaw pair faced the purple-clad Bishop of Winchester, partnered by a less elevated priest from his diocese.

'I don't believe I know you,' said the Bishop, eyeing Friar Tuck's enormous girth disapprovingly.

'We are from Nottingham, your Grace,' replied Tuck. 'I am Friar Tuck and this is Friar Robin.'

'A dangerous place, Nottingham,' declared the Bishop. 'Have you ever encountered the murderous outlaws we keep hearing about?'

Friar Tuck crossed himself. 'I trust they would not harm a poor priest,' he replied.

The Bishop turned to Friar Tuck's partner. 'The worst of them is your namesake,' he informed him. 'Robin Hood, he is called. One of the most dangerous cut-throats in the kingdom.'

Robin Hood crossed himself in turn. 'May the Lord protect me from such a villain,' he said.

The round commenced with this deal:

Game All, Dealer South.

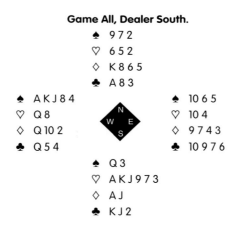

	♠	9 7 2
	♡	6 5 2
	◇	K 8 6 5
	♣	A 8 3

♠ A K J 8 4	♠ 10 6 5
♡ Q 8	♡ 10 4
◇ Q 10 2	◇ 9 7 4 3
♣ Q 5 4	♣ 10 9 7 6

	♠	Q 3
	♡	A K J 9 7 3
	◇	A J
	♣	K J 2

West	North	East	South
Bishop of	*Friar*	*Father*	*Robin*
Winchester	*Tuck*	*Benson*	*Hood*
			1♣
1♠	Dble	Pass	2♡
Pass	3♡	Pass	4♡
All Pass			

Robin Hood opened with a strong Nottingham club and the Bishop of Winchester overcalled One Spade. Friar Tuck's double showed around 5-7 points and Hood was soon installed in Four Hearts.

The Bishop led his top spades and Robin Hood ruffed the third round with the 7, retaining the 3 as a possible later entry to the dummy. When he cashed the ace of trumps both defenders followed with small cards. He then crossed to the ace of clubs and led a second round of trumps, a finesse of the jack losing to West's queen. After a few moments the Bishop decided to return a club. 'I have the remainder,' declared Hood, facing his cards.

'Good gracious,' exclaimed the Bishop. 'The man mis-plays the trump suit, then I have to give him a trick with my return.' He turned towards Robin Hood. *'Numquam novemcum, semper octocum,'* he recited. 'Were you not taught that?'

Robin Hood smiled. 'I was,' he replied, 'but this way I would make the contract wherever the queen of trumps was.'

The Bishop was not accustomed to being lectured, particularly by those several leagues below him in the church hierarchy. 'It gained you nothing at all,' he said. 'The other declarers will make the orthodox play in trumps and collect just the same ten tricks.'

'Right as always, your Grace,' declared Friar Tuck, inspecting the travelling scoresheet. 'Everyone has made +620 so far.'

The players drew their cards for the next board.

East/West Game. Dealer East.

♠ Q 10 4 2
♡ J 9 6 5 2
♢ 5
♣ A K Q

♠ 7 6   ♠ A 9 3
♡ Q 4   ♡ A 10 8 7 3
♢ K J 9 3   ♢ Q 6 2
♣ J 8 7 6 3 ♣ 10 5

♠ K J 8 5
♡ K
♢ A 10 8 7 4
♣ 9 4 2

West	North	East	South
Bishop of	*Friar*	*Father*	*Robin*
Winchester	*Tuck*	*Benson*	*Hood*
		Pass	1♢
Pass	1♡	Pass	1♠
Pass	4♠	All Pass	

With a sturdy holding in declarer's diamond suit, the Bishop decided to lead a trump. His partner won with the ace and returned a second trump, taken in the dummy.

When Robin Hood called for a heart East rose with the ace, dropping declarer's bare king. He returned a third round of trumps and Hood overtook his jack with dummy's queen. The situation did not seem promising, but when he ruffed a heart with his last trump the queen fell from West. Robin Hood now turned to dummy's club suit, arriving at this end position:

Tuck
♠ 10
♡ J 9 6
♢ 5
♣ Q

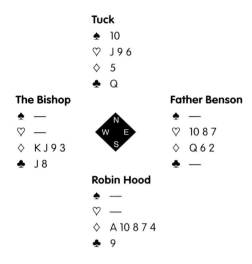

The Bishop
♠ —
♡ —
♢ K J 9 3
♣ J 8

Father Benson
♠ —
♡ 10 8 7
♢ Q 6 2
♣ —

Robin Hood
♠ —
♡ —
♢ A 10 8 7 4
♣ 9

East could not afford to throw a heart on the last club or declarer would simply duck a heart, establishing a long card in the suit. He discarded a diamond instead but Robin Hood then crossed to the ace of diamonds and ruffed a diamond, reducing East to his three hearts. A low heart threw East on lead and he had to lead into dummy's ♡J-9.

The Bishop glared suspiciously at Robin Hood. Why, the man played like a professional cardplayer. How on earth had a lowly friar acquired such a skill at the game? 'Tell me, my good man,' he demanded. 'What is the name of your friary?'

Friar Tuck intervened. 'We are itinerant friars, your Grace,' he replied. 'We belong to no friary.'

'Is your colleague deaf?' exclaimed the Bishop. 'I addressed the question to him, not to you.'

Robin Hood placed his hands together, as if in prayer. 'Our lives are devoted to the poor of Nottingham, your Grace,' he said. 'If we can win this tournament, God willing, they will not go hungry this winter.'

'I am sure the Almighty will show no-one any particular favours,' declared the Bishop. He surveyed his scorecard. 'He certainly hasn't shown us any so far.'

A round or two later Robin and Friar Tuck faced one of only two pairs of nuns competing in the event. Members of the order of St Winifred the Penniless, their habits had been handed down through the generations and were in a decidedly moth-eaten state.

'Peace be with you, Sisters,' said Robin Hood, taking his seat. 'We play the Nottingham Club.'

'May the Lord bless you and keep you, Brothers,' replied Sister Benedicta. 'Weak No-trump and the Feeble Two.'

East/West Game. Dealer North.

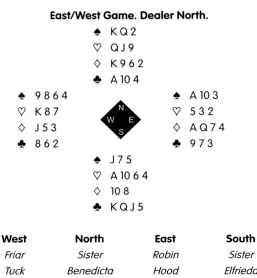

♠ K Q 2
♡ Q J 9
◇ K 9 6 2
♣ A 10 4

♠ 9 8 6 4
♡ K 8 7
◇ J 5 3
♣ 8 6 2

♠ A 10 3
♡ 5 3 2
◇ A Q 7 4
♣ 9 7 3

♠ J 7 5
♡ A 10 6 4
◇ 10 8
♣ K Q J 5

West	North	East	South
Friar	*Sister*	*Robin*	*Sister*
Tuck	*Benedicta*	*Hood*	*Elfrieda*
	1◇	Pass	3NT
All Pass			

Accustomed to stretching humble resources to the limit, Sister Elfrieda went straight to game despite holding only 11 points. Friar Tuck led ♠9 and Robin Hood won with the ace. He turned to the frail nun sitting North. 'Did your partner's 3NT response deny a four-card major?' he queried.

'Members of our order make as few bids as possible,' replied Sister Benedicta. 'We rarely respond in a suit of only four cards.'

If declarer might hold length in one or both majors, thought Robin Hood, her weakness might lie in the diamond suit. After some thought he produced a surprising card at trick two – the queen of diamonds. The 8 appeared from declarer and Friar Tuck played the 5. The elderly Sister Elfrieda won the trick with dummy's king and called for the queen of hearts. The finesse lost to Friar Tuck's king and he cashed the jack of diamonds, dropping declarer's 10. A third diamond through the dummy's 9 gave Robin Hood two more tricks in the suit and that was one down.

Sister Benedicta inspected the travelling scoresheet with no great enthusiasm. 'I fear our score on the board will be as frugal as our bidding,

Sister,' she reported. 'Everyone else seems to have made 3NT.'

'It was the queen of diamonds play which did the damage,' replied her partner. She turned to Robin Hood. You had ace-queen to four, didn't you? Why not play a low diamond?'

'I'm not sure that would be good enough,' replied Robin Hood. 'Your 10 would hold us up on the second round.'

At half-time the players stopped for some light refreshment. By the time they returned to the playing room, a scoresheet had been posted. These were the leading pairs:

1.	**Friar Tuck, Friar Robin**	**612**
2.	**Archbishop of York, Canon Bartlett**	**594**
3.	**Bishop of Winchester, Father Benson**	**552**
4.	**Brother Lucretius, Brother Magnus**	**547**

'Not much of a lead,' remarked Robin Hood, inspecting the list. 'After such a session, I thought we would be way ahead.'

'The Archbishop of York is a strong player,' replied Friar Tuck. 'I have heard it said that he is the finest rubber bridge player outside London.'

Hood and Friar Tuck performed competently on the next few rounds but no better than that. It seemed that all would turn on their fortunes in the final round, where they would face the Archbishop of York. His partner was the unsavoury Canon Bartlett, choirmaster of York Minster. It was common knowledge that his choirboys were selected on account of their good looks, rather than the purity of their singing voices.

'Ah, the mysterious Friars from Nottingham,' declared the Archbishop as Robin and Tuck took their seats. 'I'm surprised I have not heard of you. Where do you play normally?'

The Drunken Partridge alehouse would hardly be an appropriate answer, thought Tuck. 'We play cards rarely, my Lord,' he replied. 'Our time is spent in attending the poor and praying for their salvation.'

The Archbishop nodded. 'As is that of us all,' he replied.

This was the first hand of the round:

North/South Game. Dealer East.

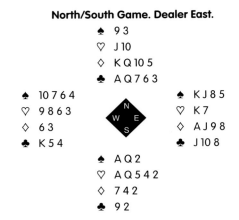

♠ 9 3
♡ J 10
◇ K Q 10 5
♣ A Q 7 6 3

♠ 10 7 6 4   ♠ K J 8 5
♡ 9 8 6 3   ♡ K 7
◇ 6 3   ◇ A J 9 8
♣ K 5 4   ♣ J 10 8

♠ A Q 2
♡ A Q 5 4 2
◇ 7 4 2
♣ 9 2

West	North	East	South
Archbishop	Friar	Canon	Robin
of York	Tuck	Bartlett	Hood
		1◇	1♡
Pass	2◇	Pass	2♡
Pass	3♡	Pass	4♡
All Pass			

The outlaw pair bid ambitiously to Four Hearts, West leading 6◇. The East player, who had a somewhat florid complexion, allowed dummy's king of diamonds to win, signalling encouragement with the 9. The jack of trumps was covered by the king and ace, Hood returning to dummy with the 10 of trumps. A successful spade finesse came next and Hood then cashed the queen of trumps, disappointed to see East show out.

The outlook was not bright as he surveyed this position:

Friar Tuck's Invitation

Tuck
- ♠ 9
- ♡ —
- ◇ Q 10 5
- ♣ A Q 7 6

Archbishop
- ♠ 10 7 6
- ♡ 9
- ◇ 3
- ♣ K 5 4

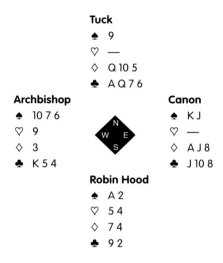

Canon
- ♠ K J
- ♡ —
- ◇ A J 8
- ♣ J 10 8

Robin Hood
- ♠ A 2
- ♡ 5 4
- ◇ 7 4
- ♣ 9 2

Robin Hood led 2♣, West following with the 4. 'Play the seven,' he said.

Canon Bartlett won with the 8 and returned the king of spades. Hood now finessed the queen of clubs successfully and discarded a spade on the ace of clubs. Both defenders followed to the trick and he was then able to discard a diamond loser on the fourth round of clubs. West ruffed with the master trump and the defenders claimed one diamond trick but this was their quota. The contract had been made.

'Nothing we could do,' declared the Archbishop. He turned disdainfully towards Robin Hood. 'Luck was certainly with you in the club suit.'

'Quite so, my Lord,' replied Hood. 'Had you risen with the king of clubs on the first round I would have been beaten.'

The Archbishop, who was entering the result on his scorecard, stopped in mid-stroke. Good gracious, it seemed that the disrespectful Friar was right. Declarer could not afford to let the king win or he would suffer the immediate loss of two diamond tricks. But if he took the king with the ace he would score only two club tricks.

On the penultimate hand of the event, with the vulnerability in his side's favour, Robin Hood picked up this miserable hand:

```
        ♠  J 8 6 2
        ♡  8 5
        ◊  7 4 2
        ♣  9 8 4 2
```

'Three Hearts,' said the Archbishop, to Hood's left.

'Double,' said Friar Tuck.

'Is that for take-out?' enquired the Canon, with a somewhat unwholesome sniff.

Hood nodded that it was and the Canon raised to Four Hearts. After two passes Friar Tuck doubled again. Hood now had to consider whether he should pass the double, hoping for four tricks in defence, or bid Four Spades. A minus score seemed a lively possibility in either case. Still, surely Friar Tuck would hold something good in spades; he was likely to have a singleton heart too. 'Four Spades,' said Robin Hood.

'No bid,' said the Archbishop.

'Six Spades,' said Friar Tuck.

There was no further bidding. The Archbishop led the king of hearts and this proved to be the full deal:

East/West Game. Dealer West.

```
                    ♠  A K Q 4
                    ♡  Void
                    ◊  A 10 5
                    ♣  A K Q 7 6 3
   ♠  9                                  ♠  10 7 5 3
   ♡  K Q J 9 7 6 3        N             ♡  A 10 4 2
   ◊  Q 6 3            W       E         ◊  K J 9 8
   ♣  10 5                   S           ♣  J
                    ♠  J 8 6 2
                    ♡  8 5
                    ◊  7 4 2
                    ♣  9 8 4 2
```

West	North	East	South
Archbishop	*Friar*	*Canon*	*Robin*
of York	*Tuck*	*Bartlett*	*Hood*
3♡	Dble	4♡	Pass
Pass	Dble	Pass	4♠
Pass	6♠	All Pass	

'I haven't overbid on this occasion, you will be pleased to hear,' announced Friar Tuck, as he laid out the dummy.

'No, indeed,' replied Robin Hood. He breathed a sigh of relief. Thank goodness he hadn't passed the double of Four Hearts. Declarer would have had seven heart tricks and some diamond tricks too. The contract might even have been made!

Hood turned his mind to the spade slam. If trumps were 3-2 there would be no problem; he could score four trumps, six clubs, the diamond ace and one heart ruff. But what if East held four trumps? After ruffing the heart lead and cashing dummy's top three trumps, the lead would be stranded in the dummy; the situation would be hopeless. Wait a minute. Perhaps there was a chance, even if East did hold four trumps.

'Ruff with the ace of trumps,' said Robin Hood.

The king of trumps came next, Robin Hood noting with interest the fall of the 9 to his left. West showed out when dummy's queen of trumps was played but this presented no problem. Hood could now lead a trump to the 8, draw East's last trump with the jack, and claim twelve tricks.

'You played it well,' congratulated Friar Tuck as he inscribed the fruits of Hood's labour on the travelling score-sheet. 'All sorts of results here. Six Clubs going down, Six Spades going down. Two pairs made Four Hearts doubled on the East-West cards!'

On the final board of the event, with the score at Love All, Friar Tuck picked up this hand:

♠ 8 5 3
♡ Q 6 5 4
◇ K 6
♣ A K 6 3

'Two Spades,' said the Archbishop, to his right.

Friar Tuck turned towards Canon Bartlett. 'That's a Strong Two, is it?' he enquired.

'No, no, we play the Feeble Two at duplicate,' replied Canon Bartlett. 'Six to ten points.'

Friar Tuck thumbed through his cards. What was he thinking about? He had nowhere near enough to come in at this level. Still, it would be a bit embarrassing if he passed now. It was obvious to everyone that he had been considering a bid. 'Double,' said Friar Tuck.

'No bid,' said Canon Bartlett.

'Six Hearts,' said Robin Hood.

Friar Tuck winced. Still, at least Robin had bid the slam in hearts, not diamonds. His hand would not be too bad in support of hearts.

This was the full deal:

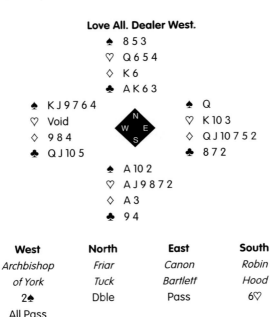

Love All. Dealer West.

♠ 853	
♥ Q654	
♦ K6	
♣ AK63	

West	East
♠ KJ9764	♠ Q
♥ Void	♥ K103
♦ 984	♦ QJ10752
♣ QJ105	♣ 872

♠ A102
♥ AJ9872
♦ A3
♣ 94

West	North	East	South
Archbishop	*Friar*	*Canon*	*Robin*
of York	*Tuck*	*Bartlett*	*Hood*
2♠	Dble	Pass	6♡
All Pass			

The Archbishop led the queen of clubs and Friar Tuck was somewhat reluctant to display his dummy. 'I barely have my bid, partner,' he said. 'I found myself thinking and then it was awkward to pass.'

Robin Hood smiled at his colleague. 'Let's see what you have, anyway,' he said.

Hood won the club lead with dummy's ace and studied the trump position. A low trump to the jack would be sufficient to pick up king doubleton with East; it would not be good enough when East held all three trumps, however. 'Queen of trumps, please,' he said.

The queen was covered by the king and ace, West showing out. The trump suit could now be picked up, thought Hood, but how could he avoid two spade losers? West's opening bid suggested that the spades were 6-1. If East held four or more clubs it would be possible to cash the spade ace and endplay him on the fourth round of clubs, discarding one spade from the South hand. The other spade loser could then be thrown on the enforced ruff-and-discard return. Still, this queen of clubs lead rather suggested that West would hold the club length.

Robin Hood crossed to dummy's remaining club honour and led ♡4, East producing the 3. Hood underplayed with the 2 and took advantage of his continued presence in the dummy by ruffing a third round of clubs. The Archbishop, sitting West, following with the jack to this trick, hoping to introduce some degree of ambiguity.

Robin Hood was still inclined to place West with the missing ♣10. For one thing, East might have signalled encouragement on the queen lead, had he held four to the 10. Hood drew East's last trump with the jack and crossed to the king of diamonds. He then ruffed dummy's last club, relieved to see that it was indeed West who followed to this trick. The ace of diamonds was cashed and these cards remained:

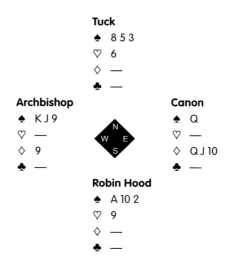

Tuck
♠ 8 5 3
♡ 6
♢ —
♣ —

Archbishop
♠ K J 9
♡ —
♢ 9
♣ —

Canon
♠ Q
♡ —
♢ Q J 10
♣ —

Robin Hood
♠ A 10 2
♡ 9
♢ —
♣ —

Robin Hood now exited with a low spade. West played the 9 and East had to overtake with the queen. The resultant ruff-and-discard allowed declarer to spirit away his remaining spade loser and the slam had been made.

'No difference if I rise with the king,' observed the Archbishop wearily.

'Your queen falls and I would have to lead back into the ace-ten.'

Canon Bartlett surveyed the Archbishop with a look he normally reserved for errant choirboys. 'Lead a spade at trick one,' he said. 'That's what we needed.'

'Had the Good Lord intended me to lead a spade,' replied the Archbishop, 'he would not have given me a solid sequence in clubs.'

A mischievous glint came to Robin Hood's eye. 'Once a club is led the contract is unbeatable,' he declared.

Canon Bartlett nodded his agreement.

'Unless, of course,' continued Hood, 'the good Canon throws his spade queen on the fourth round of clubs.'

'Of course!' cried the Archbishop. 'Good heavens, Bartlett, the poor of York will never forgive you. With your queen out of the way I can win the spade exit with the 9 and play back the king.'

The results were soon announced. Robin Hood and Friar Tuck had won by half a top, their good scores on the final round carrying them past the Archbishop and his partner. To muted applause from their fellow contestants they were presented with an armoured chest of gold coins.

'I trust you will take good care of it,' declared the Archbishop of York, none too pleased not to have won the event himself. 'If the chest were to fall into outlaw hands the noble Deacon would turn in his grave.'

This image was too much for Friar Tuck. 'We can't allow that to happen,' he replied, removing the chest from Robin Hood's grasp. 'No, I will carry it back to Nottingham myself.'

5
THE ROYAL VISITOR

The Sheriff's dresser, Edwyn, knocked nervously on the door of his master's bedchamber. No answer could be heard and he knocked more loudly.

'Yes?' came an angry cry from within.

Edwyn entered the room and bowed respectfully towards the jumble of bedclothes in the four-poster.

'What in Heaven's name do you mean by interrupting me at this hour?' demanded the Sheriff, emerging from the bedding. He glanced through the arrow-slits, assessing the sun's height. 'Why, it must be barely ten on the clock.'

'A messenger arrived from London in the middle of the night, my Lord,' replied Edwyn. 'He bore news that King John is to visit Nottingham Castle. He is bringing with him two keepers of the King's purse to collect the shire's tax revenues.'

'What?' cried the Sheriff. 'The tax accounts are nowhere near in shape. What is the intended date of the visit?'

'Today, my Lord,' replied Edwyn. 'He plans to arrive at noon.'

The Sheriff leapt out of bed. 'Are you mad to wake me so late?' he exclaimed. 'I would normally allow a week to prepare for such a visit.'

Some two hours later the sound of trumpets could be heard as the royal entourage entered Nottingham Castle on horseback.

'We are greatly honoured by your visit, my Liege,' said the Sheriff. 'I have made what arrangements I could at such short notice. A luncheon of assorted game is prepared, should you be hungry. A selection of young wenches from Lucas Street will be at your disposal tonight. Should you wish to hunt, I have a fine Arab stallion standing by…'

'You gibber like a criminal before the assizes,' declared King John, looking down from his horse. 'Why do you act in such a guilty manner? The tax revenues have met their target, I take it?'

'Er … I believe all is in order, my Liege,' replied the Sheriff. 'A little luncheon for you, perhaps?'

'I never take food immediately after a hard ride,' replied the King, dismounting. 'Perhaps we might play a little of that new game, bridge. Sir Henry Wycliffe, here, is teaching it to me.'

Gisburne was summoned to the stateroom and the game began. The King's anger was easily roused and the Sheriff was anxious that he should be allowed to win the game. No matter if this should occur due to a few mistakes on his own part. With the tax revenues in such a parlous state, looking foolish in a card game would be a small price to pay for surviving the visit unscathed.

On the first deal Sir Guy of Gisburne, sitting West, picked up these cards:

♠ 7 5 4
♡ Void
♢ 4 3
♣ A K Q J 7 6 3 2

'I bid One Spade,' said King John, to his right.

'Five Clubs,' said Gisburne.

The enormous Sir Henry Wycliffe, whose clothing was exceeded in richness only by that of the King, thumbed through his cards. 'Six Spades,' he said.

There was no further bidding and Gisburne had to find a lead. The Sheriff had not had the opportunity to brief him before the game but presumably, thought Gisburne, the idea would be to let the King win handsomely. It seemed that the safest lead, with that aim in mind, would be ♣2. The odds were 2-1 in favour of dummy or declarer holding the 10. If misfortune struck and the Sheriff held the 10, then he would surely take the 2 as suit preference for a diamond return rather than a heart. The contract would be secure in any case. Gisburne led ♣2 and down went the dummy.

Love All. Dealer South.

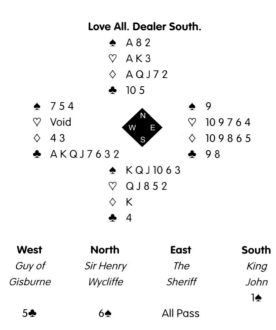

	♠ A 8 2	
	♡ A K 3	
	◇ A Q J 7 2	
	♣ 10 5	
♠ 7 5 4		♠ 9
♡ Void		♡ 10 9 7 6 4
◇ 4 3		◇ 10 9 8 6 5
♣ A K Q J 7 6 3 2		♣ 9 8
	♠ K Q J 10 6 3	
	♡ Q J 8 5 2	
	◇ K	
	♣ 4	

West	North	East	South
Guy of	*Sir Henry*	*The*	*King*
Gisburne	*Wycliffe*	*Sheriff*	*John*
			1♠
5♣	6♠	All Pass	

The King considered it beneath his dignity to play the dummy himself and was accustomed to calling the cards, as at duplicate. 'Play low,' he said.

The Sheriff contributed the 8 over dummy's 5 and was surprised to find this card winning the trick. By the Saints, that man Gisburne was a leather-brain! Obviously he was void in diamonds and was hoping for a ruff. Had he no sense of the occasion? Pointedly ignoring the suit preference signal, the Sheriff returned a heart. Gisburne ruffed and the contract was one down.

'You could have won the first trick with the 10, my Liege,' Wycliffe pointed out.

King John glared at Gisburne. 'You underled the four top honours?' he cried. 'You would make a fool of your sovereign?'

'No, no, my Liege,' replied a horrified Gisburne. 'I had a void heart, as you saw. I was hoping to put my partner on lead to obtain a ruff.'

The King spun towards the Sheriff. 'You had five in each red suit, didn't you?' he demanded. 'How did you know to return a heart instead of a diamond?'

'It was just an unlucky guess, my Liege,' replied the Sheriff. 'Er ... a lucky guess, I mean. Gisburne and I are inexperienced at the game; we scarcely know what we're doing.'

Sir Henry Wycliffe moved his side a game ahead with a competently played dummy reversal. Then this deal arose:

North/South Game. Dealer North.

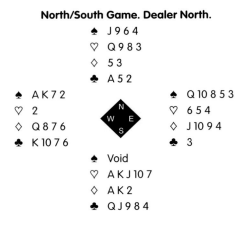

```
              ♠ J 9 6 4
              ♡ Q 9 8 3
              ♢ 5 3
              ♣ A 5 2
♠ A K 7 2                      ♠ Q 10 8 5 3
♡ 2                           ♡ 6 5 4
♢ Q 8 7 6                     ♢ J 10 9 4
♣ K 10 7 6                    ♣ 3
              ♠ Void
              ♡ A K J 10 7
              ♢ A K 2
              ♣ Q J 9 8 4
```

West	North	East	South
Guy of	*Sir Henry*	*The*	*King*
Gisburne	*Wycliffe*	*Sheriff*	*John*
	Pass	Pass	1♡
Dble	3♡	Pass	6♡
All Pass			

Gisburne was surprised that the King, who had opened only One Heart, could have enough to proceed to a slam. 'What system are you playing, my Liege?' he enquired.

'Norman methods, of course,' replied the King gruffly. 'Strong no-trump and five-card majors.'

Gisburne led the ace of spades and the King ruffed in the South hand. Trumps were drawn in three rounds, leaving him with only one trump in the dummy. Since this would be needed to ruff his losing diamond, he would have to pick up the clubs for one loser. The King led a low club to dummy's ace and called for another club, wincing when East showed out. His queen drew Gisburne's king.

Gisburne surveyed his remaining cards. How could he allow the contract to make without arousing suspicion? It was a pity he had been so recently informed that the opponents were playing a five-card major system. He might otherwise have played a club into declarer's tenace, claiming that he hoped East held another trump. Perhaps a diamond would be the best shot, playing declarer for A-K-J in the suit.

Gisburne's diamond return went to the 9 and ace. The King now cashed the jack of clubs and ruffed a club, returning to his hand with a spade ruff. These cards were outstanding:

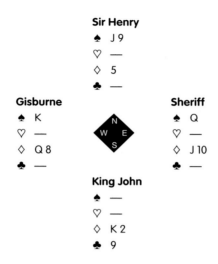

Sir Henry
♠ J 9
♡ —
♢ 5
♣ —

Gisburne
♠ K
♡ —
♢ Q 8
♣ —

Sheriff
♠ Q
♡ —
♢ J 10
♣ —

King John
♠ —
♡ —
♢ K 2
♣ 9

When the King cashed his last club Gisburne and the Sheriff had to adopt desperate measures to allow the contract to succeed. They both threw a diamond, retaining a spade honour. The queen and jack of diamonds now fell under declarer's king and his ♢2 was left a winner.

'A double squeeze, my Liege!' exclaimed the Sheriff. 'Excellently played. We both had to retain a spade to guard against the dummy's jack.'

The King guffawed in delight. 'You bumble-heads!' he cried. 'There was no entry to the dummy. You could simply have thrown your spade guards!'

Sir Henry Wycliffe joined in the merriment. 'The most idiotic defence I've ever witnessed, my Liege,' he declared. 'I'm surprised you entrust the gathering of the region's tax to such lamb-brains.'

The Sheriff gritted his teeth. The contract should have been made anyway, he thought. The silly old fool had misplayed the clubs. He should have run the queen on the first round, planning to run the 9 on the next round should the queen hold. The line would lose only to a singleton king with East.

The King, meanwhile, had reached for his scoring quill. 'Excellent,' he declared. 'The first rubber comes to 24 sovereigns apiece.'

The Sheriff's mouth dropped. This was a considerable sum, even for a man of his standing. 'I hadn't realised we were playing for money, my Liege,' he said. 'Not for such high stakes, anyway.'

Gisburne, by no means a man of wealth, swallowed nervously. 'Is it not normal to agree stakes before the play starts?' he queried.

'Do you think I am soft in the head?' cried the King. 'You think I would agree to stakes of one sovereign a point before I knew how useless you were at the game?' He raised his eyes disbelievingly to the ceiling. 'You might have been experts, for all I knew.'

The door swung open and in walked two thin, dour-faced men. 'We are ready to perform our duties, my Liege,' said Lionel Wolfe, the taller of the two. He turned towards the Sheriff. 'We will need access to your treasure chamber to collect the appointed amount.'

'The total set for the shire was two thousand seven hundred sovereigns,' added the other man.

The Sheriff steeled himself to address the King. 'My men did collect that amount, my Liege,' he said. 'But unfortunately, due to several raids and hold-ups by the outlaws led by Robin Hood, we are now an amount, a small amount, short of that mark.'

'By the fires of Hell!' cried the King, rising to his feet. 'Were you not able to retrieve the money when you captured this Robin Hood?'

'There is one small problem with that, my Liege,' replied the Sheriff. 'The Captain of the Guard assigned to the task has not yet managed to capture Robin Hood.'

'Then the man should be whipped until he is senseless!' thundered the King. 'After that he should then be stretched on the rack for several hours, hung, drawn and quartered.'

The King turned towards Gisburne. 'The Sheriff should not have to trouble himself with such incompetent underlings,' he declared. 'You will make yourself personally responsible for seeing that this punishment is administered.'

Gisburne had gone pale. 'I will see to it, my Liege,' he replied.

'How do you wish us to proceed?' enquired Lionel Wolfe.

'Collect every penny you can find,' replied the King. 'The Sheriff, here, will be personally responsible for the balance.'

The two morose tax collectors left the room. 'Now, let's continue this enjoyable game,' said the King. 'You want to reduce the stakes, do I take it?'

Feeling that the storm had abated, the Sheriff saw no harm in retrieving a little something from the wreckage. 'No, I found the experience invigorating, my Liege,' he replied. 'Shall we make it five sovereigns a point?'

Play recommenced at these exalted stakes and the Sheriff soon found himself at the helm of a slam.

Love All. Dealer South.

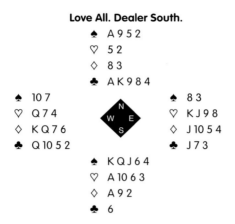

North
♠ A 9 5 2
♡ 5 2
◇ 8 3
♣ A K 9 8 4

West
♠ 10 7
♡ Q 7 4
◇ K Q 7 6
♣ Q 10 5 2

East
♠ 8 3
♡ K J 9 8
◇ J 10 5 4
♣ J 7 3

South
♠ K Q J 6 4
♡ A 10 6 3
◇ A 9 2
♣ 6

West	North	East	South
King John	*Guy of Gisburne*	*Sir Henry Wycliffe*	*The Sheriff*
			1♠
Pass	2♣	Pass	2♡
Pass	4♠	Pass	4NT
Pass	5♡	Pass	6♠
All Pass			

'What means this bidding?' demanded King John. 'If the man's hand was strong enough to bid Four Spades all along, why did he not do so straight away?'

The Sheriff had no intention of discussing with his monarch the theory of delayed game raises. For one thing, he wanted to appear a novice at the game for as long as possible. 'Presumably he mis-sorted his hand, my Liege,' he replied. 'He must have had one of his spades in with the clubs.'

King John led the king of diamonds and down went the dummy. The Sheriff was disappointed to find no red-suit singleton there. It was annoying, too, that the King had led a diamond rather than a heart. On a heart lead a 2-2 trump break might have been enough to make the contract. After conceding a heart he would have had two heart ruffs available as entries to the dummy; there would have been a good chance of setting up a long club as a twelfth trick.

After a few moments inspiration struck. The Sheriff won the king of diamonds lead with the ace, crossed to the ace of clubs, and ruffed a club high. Seeking an extra entry to the dummy, he then played a trump to the 9. The finesse succeeded and he proceeded to ruff another club high, both defenders following. Muttering a small prayer, the Sheriff led a second round of trumps to dummy's ace. Yes! Both defenders followed. He could now discard two diamond losers on the king of clubs and the long club. A diamond ruff in the South hand brought his total to twelve tricks.

'Upon my soul, you are the luckiest player alive!' exclaimed the King. 'If my partner had held the 10 you would have lost a trump trick, despite holding the four top honours.'

'Yes, I see, my Liege,' replied the Sheriff.

'Your partner's lunacy must be contagious,' continued the King. 'He underled his four top honours only a short while ago, trying to lose a trick to the 10.'

On the next deal the King went down in a cold 3NT, taking a queen finesse into the danger hand rather than the safe hand. Nine tricks would have been assured had he taken the finesse the other way.

'Damn and blast!' exclaimed the King. 'The man held six spades to his partner's two. You told me only last week, Henry, that the man with the shorter holding would be favourite to hold any missing honour card.'

Sir Henry measured his words carefully. 'Quite so, my Liege,' he replied. 'You played cleverly. I fear that virtue will have to be its own reward on the hand.'

This was the next deal:

North/South Game. Dealer East.

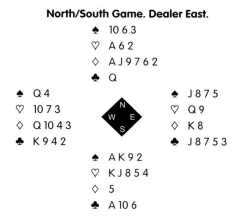

	♠ 10 6 3	
	♡ A 6 2	
	◊ A J 9 7 6 2	
	♣ Q	
♠ Q 4		♠ J 8 7 5
♡ 10 7 3		♡ Q 9
◊ Q 10 4 3		◊ K 8
♣ K 9 4 2		♣ J 8 7 5 3
	♠ A K 9 2	
	♡ K J 8 5 4	
	◊ 5	
	♣ A 10 6	

West	North	East	South
King	*Guy of*	*Sir Henry*	*The*
John	*Gisburne*	*Wycliffe*	*Sheriff*
		Pass	1♡
Pass	2◊	Pass	2♠
Pass	4♡	Pass	4NT
Pass	5♡	Pass	6♡
All Pass			

'By Saint Athanasius, the man does it again!' cried the King. 'Why did he not raise to Four Hearts directly? Did he have a heart sorted with his diamonds this time?'

The Sheriff shrugged his shoulders in a gesture of helplessness. 'With Gisburne anything is possible, my Liege,' he replied.

The King led a low trump and the Sheriff inspected the dummy closely. It seemed that he would need to ruff two clubs in dummy, then play for one spade loser. But, if he ran the trump lead to his hand, one of the club ruffs would have to be taken with the ace; he would then have a loser on the third round of trumps. What could be done?

The Sheriff soon spotted the best chance. He won the trump lead with dummy's ace, crossed to the ace of clubs, and ruffed a club. A spade to the ace allowed him to ruff his last club and he re-entered his hand with the spade king. On this trick he was pleased to see the queen of spades fall from West. An even greater treat awaited him on the next trick. When he cashed the king of trumps, the other major-suit queen appeared, this time from East. The Sheriff now played a spade to the 10 and jack, establishing ♠9 as a twelfth trick.

'I'faith, the man has the luck of the Devil,' declared the King. 'The very moment we increase the stakes, Wycliffe, it really is too much.'

Sir Henry Wycliffe was beginning to realise that there was rather more than luck behind the Sheriff's two pieces of dummy play. 'Perhaps we should stop playing, my Liege,' he suggested. 'The sun shines. An afternoon's hunting would be entertaining.'

'You think these two dunces deserve a handful of my gold?'

'Er ... no, my Liege,' replied Wycliffe.

'In that case we will retrieve the losses,' declared the King. 'Instead of assessing the weather you should pay more attention to your game, Wycliffe. You have been playing poorly.'

The King was pleased to see a change of fortune at the start of the next rubber, Wycliffe scoring game in spades. Gisburne levelled matters with a straightforward 3NT, then the biggest hand of the afternoon arose.

Game All. Dealer South.

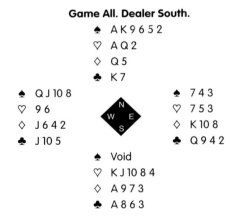

```
              ♠ A K 9 6 5 2
              ♡ A Q 2
              ◇ Q 5
              ♣ K 7
♠ Q J 10 8                      ♠ 7 4 3
♡ 9 6            N              ♡ 7 5 3
◇ J 6 4 2     W   E            ◇ K 10 8
♣ J 10 5          S            ♣ Q 9 4 2
              ♠ Void
              ♡ K J 10 8 4
              ◇ A 9 7 3
              ♣ A 8 6 3
```

West	North	East	South
King	*Guy of*	*Sir Henry*	*The*
John	*Gisburne*	*Wycliffe*	*Sheriff*
			1♡
Pass	2♠	Pass	3♣
Pass	4NT	Pass	5♡
Pass	5NT	Pass	6♢
Pass	7♡	All Pass	

When the Sheriff admitted to only one king, Gisburne paused for a moment. Surely it would be unlucky in the extreme if the king were in diamonds and the opening bid had been on a jack-high suit. The Sheriff would never forgive him if they missed an absolutely cold grand slam at these stakes. 'Seven Hearts,' said Sir Guy of Gisburne.

'A plague on this pack!' exclaimed the King. 'I have never seen such a run of cards in one direction.'

Sir Henry Wycliffe was not looking at all well. Did the King expect him to pay his own losses? It had not been his decision to play for such exorbitant stakes. It was becoming increasingly obvious with each deal that the opponents were very strong players. Not that the King appeared to have realised it yet. 'It is your lead, my Liege,' he said.

The King led the queen of spades. Gisburne laid out the dummy and watched anxiously as the Sheriff made his early calculations. From the time he was taking to play to the first trick it seemed that the slam was not exactly lay-down.

The Sheriff saw that if spades were 4-3 he could establish the suit and reach it easily enough. Five hearts in his hand, four spades in the dummy, and three minor-suit winners would bring the total to only twelve, however. One or more club ruffs could not be added to this total because it would not then be possible to draw trumps before running the spade suit. Could the thirteenth trick come from a squeeze? Not very likely. For a squeeze to work, it seemed East would need to hold the diamond king and no fewer than five clubs.

The first step in any case must surely be to set up the spades, decided the Sheriff. He ruffed the spade lead in his hand and crossed to the ace of trumps. On this trick the 6 fell from West, the 3 from East. The Sheriff studied these spot-cards carefully. The most likely distribution of the trumps on this evidence was that West held two and East three. In that case he could see a possible route to thirteen tricks.

The Sheriff ruffed a second spade in his hand, then crossed to dummy's queen of trumps. The 9 fell from West, the 5 from East, confirming the Sheriff's view of the trump suit.

With a trump still at large, the Sheriff proceeded to run dummy's spade suit. Sir Henry Wycliffe had nowhere near enough safe cards to throw on the spades. In fact he decided to ruff the fourth round. The Sheriff overruffed and returned to dummy with the king of clubs. East threw a diamond on the fifth round of spades and these cards remained:

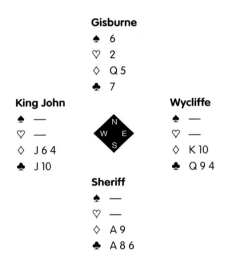

Gisburne
- ♠ 6
- ♡ 2
- ◇ Q 5
- ♣ 7

King John
- ♠ —
- ♡ —
- ◇ J 6 4
- ♣ J 10

Wycliffe
- ♠ —
- ♡ —
- ◇ K 10
- ♣ Q 9 4

Sheriff
- ♠ —
- ♡ —
- ◇ A 9
- ♣ A 8 6

The last spade left Wycliffe with no good discard. Recalling that the Sheriff had bid clubs during the auction and would surely ruff the suit good if he threw a club, Wycliffe decided to throw ◇10.

There were still five clubs out, so the Sheriff knew that there was no future in retaining that suit, hoping to ruff a long card good. He discarded a club on the last spade, then reached for dummy's 5. The appearance of East's king of diamonds on this trick was one of the most pleasurable sights of his life. The Sheriff won with the ace and exultantly claimed the remaining tricks. After such a hand, he thought, one could die happy.

'Am I partnering a madman?' cried the King, rising angrily to his feet. 'Keep a guard on the diamond king, Wycliffe, and he is one down. Are you in league with them?'

'There was nothing I could do, my Liege,' protested Wycliffe. 'He makes thirteen tricks whatever I throw. It was a squeeze.'

'A squeeze? What in the Devil's name is that?' demanded the King.

'We have not yet come to it in my instruction,' replied Wycliffe. Nor, he forebore to add, had they covered opening leads against a grand slam. Had a trump been led, declarer's line of play would have been impossible.

The oak door to the stateroom swung open and two tax collectors entered once more. 'We have taken all the gold and coins, my Liege,' Lionel Wolfe declared. 'Also all the jewellery and spices, assessing the appropriate monetary value.'

'Very good,' declared the King. 'And what was the final total?'

The other tax collector assumed a severe expression. 'It was well short of the target, my Liege,' he replied. 'Some three hundred and twenty pounds short.'

The Sheriff looked up triumphantly from his scoring pad. 'The last two rubbers amount to some three hundred and thirty two pounds between you, my Liege,' he said. 'It seems that will cover the shortfall.'

The King and his party departed the next day and the Sheriff and Gisburne proceeded to celebrate the affair with several jugs of strong porter.

'What will you do for money, my Lord?' enquired Gisburne, his speech slurred by the drink. 'Your treasure chamber is empty; they have cleaned you out.'

The Sheriff laughed. 'Sometimes you are as foolish as the King himself,' he replied. 'Do you think I keep all my money where it can be found?'

'Excellent, my Lord!' declared Gisburne. His face then clouded over. 'But what about the King's instructions with regard to the Commander of the Guard? Drawing and quartering would seem a little harsh after my invaluable assistance in the card game. Not everyone would have bid that grand slam in hearts.'

The Sheriff gazed fondly at his second-in-command. 'Nor would they,' he replied. 'Very well, we will postpone the King's recommendation for a month. I'm sure you will have Hood under lock and key by then.'

6
THE FIVE ANGELS TAVERN

obin Hood and Nazir peered into the smoky interior of the Five Angels tavern. Several games were in progress and they recognised most of the protagonists. In the far corner two moderate players faced a couple of wealthy-looking strangers, unknown to Hood.

'Their fur coats are worth ten sovereigns apiece, for a start,' observed Robin Hood. 'Should be some rich pickings here.'

The outlaws ordered two tankards of ale and took a seat a couple of tables away from the game that had attracted their interest. It was not going well for the two local players, who had been at loggerheads more than once before the rubber drew to a close. They found enough money to settle their losses, then made their way out of the tavern. Hood strolled casually towards the two strangers.

'What game were you playing there, my friends?' he enquired. 'Chase the Queen, was it?'

'Never heard of it,' replied the man in the corner, speaking with a strong Irish accent. 'No, we were playing bridge. You know it?'

'Chase the Queen's more fun,' replied Hood. 'You deal out 10 cards each, then everyone chooses four cards to pass to the player on his left…'

The other stranger, who had an unhealthy greyish-yellow complexion, glared at Hood. 'Don't waste our time, fellow,' he said, also in a heavy Irish accent. 'We only play bridge.'

'Let's take them on, Nazir,' said Robin Hood. 'What are the stakes? A penny a 100, shall we make it?'

'Don't waste our time, I said,' snarled the ill-looking one. 'We don't play for less than a shilling a 100.'

'Very well,' agreed Hood.

The first rubber began and neither side had yet made game when Robin Hood arrived in Six Spades.

Love All. Dealer West.

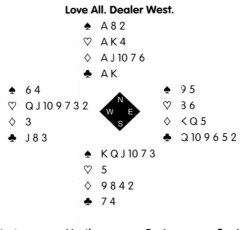

```
              ♠ A 8 2
              ♡ A K 4
              ◇ A J 10 7 6
              ♣ A K
   ♠ 6 4                      ♠ 9 5
   ♡ Q J 10 9 7 3 2           ♡ 3 6
   ◇ 3                        ◇ < Q 5
   ♣ J 8 3                    ♣ Q 10 9 6 5 2
              ♠ K Q J 10 7 3
              ♡ 5
              ◇ 9 8 4 2
              ♣ 7 4
```

West	North	East	South
Greyface	*Nazir*	*Thomas*	*Robin*
O'Donnell		*Flynne*	*Hood*
3♡	3NT	Pass	4♠
Pass	6♠	All Pass	

O'Donnell led the queen of hearts, won in the dummy, and Hood proceeded to draw trumps. When they broke 2-2 he saw that twelve tricks could be made on a simple elimination. He could cash dummy's club winners, cash the remaining high heart in dummy, throwing a diamond, then ruff the last heart. He could then play a diamond to the jack, endplaying East. Still, thought Hood, that wouldn't bring in much at one shilling stakes. No, he and Nazir had bigger ideas in mind.

At trick four, Robin Hood played a diamond to the jack and queen. When Flynne returned a heart, Hood ruffed in the South hand and led a second diamond. 'What bad luck!' he exclaimed, when West showed out. 'I must go one down now. The contract was cold unless both diamonds were offside.'

'You did all you could,' said Nazir.

Flynne glared at his partner. 'He could have made it on that heart lead,' he complained. 'Why didn't you lead the singleton diamond?'

'What difference would that make, you numskull?' cried Greyface O'Donnell. 'He wins the diamond ace and endplays me with the third heart. It's an easy make on any lead.'

'No, no, I went one down,' replied Hood. 'I could have made it, had you held one of the diamonds.'

Playing in similar fashion, Hood and Nazir managed to lose the first two rubbers.

'You cleaned out yet?' enquired O'Donnell, raking in the handful of silver won on the second rubber.

Hood laughed and produced a leather purse from his pocket. He undid the purse string and allowed O'Donnell to glimpse inside. The Irishman could not believe what he saw. By Saint Patrick! If that purse contained less than forty pounds in gold, every Dublin girl was a virgin.

O'Donnell caught his partner's eye. 'Tom and I have played long enough, I think,' he said. 'We only play shilling games for light relief. If you want another rubber or two, we'll have to be raising the stakes.'

Flynne nodded his agreement. 'Dat's right,' he said. 'Two sovereigns a 100 or we don't play no more.'

Hood looked across at Nazir. 'What do you think, partner?' he said. 'Will our luck change for the better?'

Nazir shrugged his shoulders. 'Why not?' he replied. 'Good luck follows bad luck, as often as not.'

As the next rubber started, a close observer would have noted an altogether different light in the outlaws' eyes. Losing at these stakes would be a serious business. This was the first hand:

Love All. Dealer West.

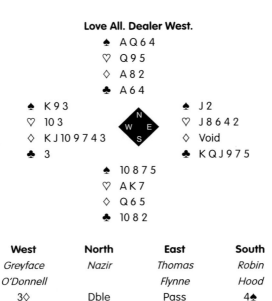

```
              ♠ A Q 6 4
              ♡ Q 9 5
              ◇ A 8 2
              ♣ A 6 4
  ♠ K 9 3                   ♠ J 2
  ♡ 10 3          N         ♡ J 8 6 4 2
  ◇ K J 10 9 7 4 3  W   E   ◇ Void
  ♣ 3              S        ♣ K Q J 9 7 5
              ♠ 10 8 7 5
              ♡ A K 7
              ◇ Q 6 5
              ♣ 10 8 2
```

West	North	East	South
Greyface	*Nazir*	*Thomas*	*Robin*
O'Donnell		*Flynne*	*Hood*
3◇	Dble	Pass	4♠
All Pass			

O'Donnell led his singleton club and down went the dummy. The matching 4-3-3-3 shape was a disappointment to Hood. How on earth could he conjure ten tricks from the two hands? One thing was certain; if he ducked the first trick he would run into an immediate cross-ruff. He reached for dummy's ace of clubs, crossed to a top heart, and took a successful finesse in trumps. The ace of trumps dropped the jack from East, leaving the king in the West hand.

Robin Hood began to see light at the end of the tunnel. West had no clubs remaining. If his hearts were removed, he would have to play on diamonds when he was thrown in. Hood cashed the two remaining heart winners, West declining to ruff the third round. This position had been reached:

Nazir
♠ 6 4
♡ —
♢ A 8 2
♣ 6 4

O'Donnell
♠ K
♡ —
♢ K J 10 9 7 4
♣ —

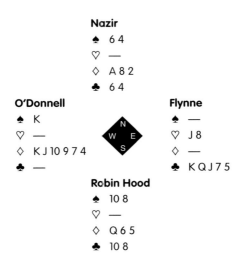

Flynne
♠ —
♡ J 8
♢ —
♣ K Q J 7 5

Robin Hood
♠ 10 8
♡ —
♢ Q 6 5
♣ 10 8

Robin Hood played a trump to West's king and the Irishman exited with the jack of diamonds. This was run successfully to the queen and Hood now played ace and another diamond, endplaying West for the second time. The enforced diamond return gave declarer a ruff-and-discard. Only one club trick would now be lost and the game was home.

'A lucky one for us,' declared Robin Hood. He turned to Grey-Face O'Donnell. 'I was bare in clubs after your lead. Another club would have put me down.'

'St Anne preserve us!' exclaimed the Irishman. 'Of course I'd play another club if I had one. I only started with one club.'

This was the next hand:

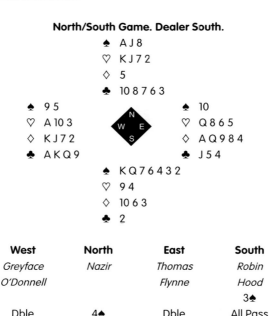

North/South Game. Dealer South.

```
              ♠ A J 8
              ♥ K J 7 2
              ◇ 5
              ♣ 10 8 7 6 3
   ♠ 9 5                      ♠ 10
   ♥ A 10 3                   ♥ Q 8 6 5
   ◇ K J 7 2                  ◇ A Q 9 8 4
   ♣ A K Q 9                  ♣ J 5 4
              ♠ K Q 7 6 4 3 2
              ♥ 9 4
              ◇ 10 6 3
              ♣ 2
```

West	North	East	South
Greyface	*Nazir*	*Thomas*	*Robin*
O'Donnell		*Flynne*	*Hood*
			3♠
Dble	4♠	Dble	All Pass

Robin Hood opened with a pre-emptive Three Spades, doubled for take-out by West. When Nazir raised to Four Spades the Irishman in the East seat had an awkward call to make. Eleven tricks might be possible on the East-West cards but how could he locate the best fit? In years to come, 4NT would perhaps indicate a two-suiter; East could start with that, correcting a Five Club response to Five Diamonds. In the latter stages of the eleventh century, however, 4NT had only one meaning – the Richmond ace-ask.

'Double,' said Thomas Flynne.

There was no further bidding and Greyface O'Donnell led the ace of clubs. At trick two he switched to a trump, won by dummy's ace. Only one diamond ruff in dummy would now be possible, so Hood set about establishing dummy's club suit. He ruffed a club, crossed to dummy's jack of trumps, and ruffed another club. He then led a heart towards dummy. O'Donnell gave nothing away, playing low smoothly, but Hood knew that most of the high cards were to his left. He reached for dummy's king, winning the trick. A third club ruff was followed by a diamond ruff and the established club was now the game-going trick.

'First rubber at two-sov stakes and you blow it!' exclaimed Flynne. 'Lead a trump, you berk, then you can play a second trump when you win the club.'

'Don't speak to me like that,' replied O'Donnell. 'You screwed the bidding, anyway. We were cold for Five Diamonds.'

It had been a lightning-quick first rubber. The two Irishmen settled up and Hood rose to his feet. 'Very enjoyable,' he declared. 'Quite exciting to play for such high stakes, I must say.'

'Where are you going?' demanded Greyface O'Donnell. 'You can't duck out of the game after only two hands.'

'Stop playing when you're ahead,' replied Hood. 'That's my motto.'

'Sit down!' cried O'Donnell threateningly.

Robin Hood resumed his seat and another high-stake rubber commenced. The Irishmen scored an early game, then Hood arrived in a slam.

East/West Game. Dealer West.

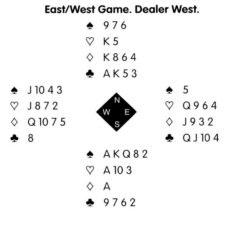

West	North	East	South
Greyface	*Nazir*	*Thomas*	*Robin*
O'Donnell		*Flynne*	*Hood*
Pass	1NT	Pass	3♠
Pass	4♣	Pass	6♠
All Pass			

O'Donnell was none too pleased to find his opponents in a slam contract. 'What in Heaven's name was this Four Club bid?' he demanded.

'A small fancy of ours,' replied Hood. 'We play that it agrees the spades as trumps and shows the ace of clubs.'

The Irishmen exchanged a glance. 'I thought you said you were beginners at the game,' said Flynne.

'We wouldn't play at these stakes if we were beginners,' replied Robin Hood. 'No, we've been playing for almost six months now.'

O'Donnell led ♣8, dummy's ace winning and East contributing the 4. Unless West had found an unusual opening shot from Q-10-8, it seemed that the opening lead must be a singleton. All would be well if trumps were 3-2; declarer could ruff his heart loser and throw a club on the diamond king. What could be done if West's singleton club was accompanied by four trumps, though? Perhaps there was still a chance.

'Get on with it,' exclaimed Greyface O'Donnell. 'Time is money.'

Robin Hood crossed to the ace of diamonds, returned to dummy with the king of hearts, and cashed the king of diamonds, throwing a club. He then ruffed a diamond in the South hand. Ace of hearts and a heart ruff permitted a second diamond ruff in the South hand, both defenders following. These cards remained:

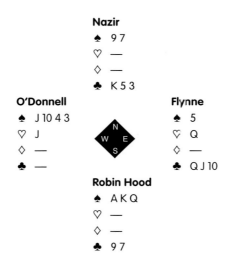

Nazir
♠ 9 7
♡ —
♢ —
♣ K 5 3

O'Donnell
♠ J 10 4 3
♡ J
♢ —
♣ —

Flynne
♠ 5
♡ Q
♢ —
♣ Q J 10

Robin Hood
♠ A K Q
♡ —
♢ —
♣ 9 7

The preparatory work at an end, Robin Hood now led a second round of clubs towards dummy's king. If West let this pass, declarer's three top trumps would bring his total to twelve. O'Donnell ruffed the club trick but had no constructive return. He chose to play a heart but Robin Hood ruffed in the dummy and discarded his last club. He then faced his sequence of trump honours, claiming the contract.

The two Irishmen were looking slightly dazed. Surely that contract had been destined to go down. Declarer had an unavoidable club loser and a second loser in trumps. The two losers had somehow been married into one.

A hand or two later, with the score still at Game All, Robin Hood picked up a truly magnificent hand.

Game All. Dealer East.

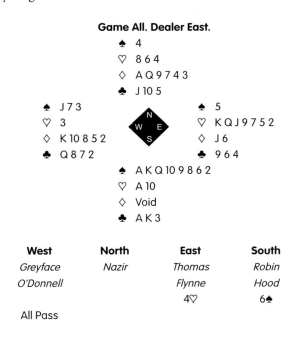

	North		
	♠ 4		
	♡ 8 6 4		
	◇ A Q 9 7 4 3		
	♣ J 10 5		

West: ♠ J 7 3 ♡ 3 ◇ K 10 8 5 2 ♣ Q 8 7 2

East: ♠ 5 ♡ K Q J 9 7 5 2 ◇ J 6 ♣ 9 6 4

South: ♠ A K Q 10 9 8 6 2 ♡ A 10 ◇ Void ♣ A K 3

West	North	East	South
Greyface	*Nazir*	*Thomas*	*Robin*
O'Donnell		*Flynne*	*Hood*
		4♡	6♠
All Pass			

Robin Hood leapt straight to Six Spades over the Irishman's pre-empt and this bid was passed out. West led ♡3 and Hood won East's jack with the ace. Dummy was a disappointment. It contained a precious ace but there appeared to be no way to reach it. Unless …

Both defenders followed to the ace of trumps and Hood continued with the king, East showing out. Robin Hood feigned a look of annoyance. 'Just our luck, partner,' he said. 'Our friend here has four trumps to the jack.'

O'Donnell surveyed the scene impassively. Stupid fool, he thought. Fancy playing for two gold ones at 100 when you can't even count trumps properly.

Hood placed the 10 of trumps on the table, O'Donnell grabbing the trick with the jack. He looked suspiciously at Robin Hood. Could the throw-in possibly be intended? The Irishman turned his mind to how he should come off lead. If declarer had deliberately surrendered an unnecessary trick in the trump suit, he must be hoping that two tricks would come back in the wash. For the play to make sense, he presumably held A-K-x in clubs and a void diamond. Yes, and in that case a diamond exit would put him to a guess.

The Irishman flipped ♢8 on to the table. It was an annoying card, thought Hood. On a club exit he would have been able to claim the contract. Should he put up the ace and run the jack of clubs? Or should he finesse the diamond queen? The club finesse scarcely looked the better chance. For one thing, if East did hold the club queen there was a fair chance that it would drop in two rounds anyway. Hood reached for the queen of diamonds and Flynne was unable to beat this card. Hood discarded a heart and a club on the diamonds and claimed the remainder. Another gold-plated rubber had come to an end.

'What do you reckon, Flynne?' said O'Donnell. 'You think these boys have been havin' us on?'

'That's thirty-two sovereigns apiece, I make it,' said Robin Hood.

'You bleedin' tricksters!' cried O'Donnell, rising to his feet. 'You led us into it, you're professionals.'

'So they are,' declared Flynne. He spat defiantly onto the floor. 'They can whistle for their money.'

'Just one minute, my friends,' exclaimed Nazir. 'You would perhaps be interested to see these.' His cloak fell open to reveal two Arab daggers. 'Each one sharp as a razor, as many victims will testify.'

Robin Hood also had a blade glinting in his hand. 'You were beaten fair and square,' he said. 'That will be thirty-two each, plus another five for our trouble in collecting it.'

The Irishmen's eyes met. 'Pay him,' said Flynne.

As the two outlaws headed for the exit, Robin Hood sent a silver coin spinning towards the owner of the establishment. 'A drink for my two friends in the corner, Landlord!' he cried. 'They look as if they need one, don't you think?'

7
THE MICHAELMAS INDIVIDUAL

On the first Saturday after Michaelmas it was the custom to hold an individual tournament in Wykham Village. The event took place in a large barn, with a mixture of villagers and outlaws participating.

'Why can't I play?' protested Gareth, youngest son of Wylfred the butcher.

His father, who was brushing the flies off a recently cut pig's head, made no reply.

'I said, why can't I play?' repeated Gareth. 'I know how to play bridge.'

His father laughed. 'You'll be needed to help guard the approach roads to the village,' he replied. 'Know how to play, indeed! It takes years to learn the game.'

Play began promptly at 2 o'clock and on the first round Robin Hood found himself sharing a table with the minstrel, Alan A'Dale. The four was completed by two villagers, young Robert Gorsham and his mother Aegwyn Gorsham. One hand would be played in partnership with each of other occupants of the table.

This was the first hand of the round:

North/South Game. Dealer South.

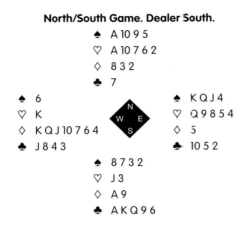

♠ A 10 9 5
♡ A 10 7 6 2
♢ 8 3 2
♣ 7

♠ 6
♡ K
♢ K Q J 10 7 6 4
♣ J 8 4 3

♠ K Q J 4
♡ Q 9 8 5 4
♢ 5
♣ 10 5 2

♠ 8 7 3 2
♡ J 3
♢ A 9
♣ A K Q 9 6

West	North	East	South
Aegwyn	*Alan*	*Robert*	*Robin*
Gorsham	*A'Dale*	*Gorsham*	*Hood*
			2♣
2♢	2♡	Pass	2♠
Pass	3♠	Pass	4♠
Pass	Pass	Dble	All Pass

Robin Hood opened Two Clubs, which in the Nottingham Club system showed 11-15 points and at least five clubs. He was soon in Four Spades, doubled by Master Gorsham in the East seat.

'Be it my lead?' asked Aegwyn Gorsham.

Reassured on that matter, she led the king of diamonds and Hood won with the ace. He cashed three top clubs, discarding dummy's remaining diamonds, then led a heart. The king showed from West and dummy's ace won the trick. When Hood led another round of hearts from the dummy, East rose with the queen. West discarded a diamond and Robert Gorsham returned a third round of hearts. Hood ruffed carefully with the 8 and viewed West's inability to overruff with mixed emotions.

A trump to the 6, 10 and jack left East on lead in this end position:

The Michaelmas Individual

Alan
♠ A 9 5
♡ 10 7
♦ —
♣ —

Aegwyn
♠ —
♡ —
♦ Q J 10 7
♣ J

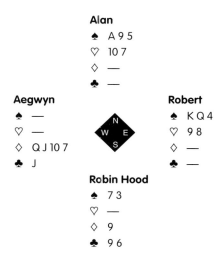

Robert
♠ K Q 4
♡ 9 8
♦ —
♣ —

Robin Hood
♠ 7 3
♡ —
♦ 9
♣ 9 6

A trump return, high or low, would make life easy for declarer; he would be able to cash ♡10, ruff dummy's last heart in his hand, then concede just one trump trick. East decided to return ♡9. Hood won with the 10, ruffed dummy's last heart with the 3 and passed the 7 of trumps to East. On lead with the queen of trumps, Robert Gorsham had to lead from his ♠K-4 into dummy's ♠A-9. Ten tricks had been made.

'You normally play better than that, Robert,' said Aegwyn Gorsham. 'Why did you put in the queen on the second round of hearts? You set up the 10 in dummy.'

'I'd be mad not to put in the queen,' her son replied Robert. 'I 'ad three certain trump tricks to go with it, or so I thought.'

'Play low and I can ruff over 'ere,' continued Aegwyn. She turned towards Robin Hood, smiling as she shook her head. 'These youngsters don't stop to think, do they? If Robert 'olds off the queen we get a nice top.'

Hood returned the smile, saying nothing. It occurred to him that she might also have scored a nice top by ruffing her partner's queen of hearts and playing a diamond through. It would no longer have been possible to eliminate dummy's hearts and achieve the trump endplay.

'They just don't stop to think,' muttered Aegwyn again.

Robert Gorsham enjoyed the briefest of partnerships with Robin Hood, the next hand being thrown in. On the final hand of the round Robin Hood would partner Aegwyn Gorsham. This was a moment for her to savour. She patted her hair into shape and attempted an alluring smile. 'I'm expectin' a good score on this one,' she said. 'You're the best player for miles around, everyone says.'

'I'll do my best.' replied Robin Hood.

Love All. Dealer East.

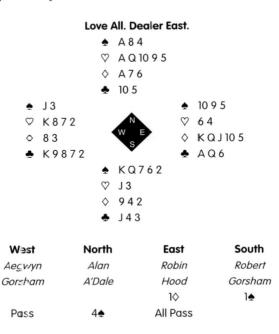

♠ A 8 4
♡ A Q 10 9 5
◇ A 7 6
♣ 10 5

♠ J 3
♡ K 8 7 2
◇ 8 3
♣ K 9 8 7 2

♠ 10 9 5
♡ 6 4
◇ K Q J 10 5
♣ A Q 6

♠ K Q 7 6 2
♡ J 3
◇ 9 4 2
♣ J 4 3

West	North	East	South
Aecwyn	Alan	Robin	Robert
Gorsham	A'Dale	Hood	Gorsham
		1◇	1♠
Pass	4♠	All Pass	

Robert Gorsham arrived in Four Spades and his mother led ◇8. 'Ace, please,' he said

The contract was a poor one. At first glance it seemed that declarer would need to be able to draw trumps in three rounds, then find West with three or fewer hearts to the king. The youngster thought he could see an extra chance. He drew just one round of trumps, with the king, then advanced the jack of hearts. There could be no point in West covering and she played low. Declarer's jack won the trick and he continued with a heart to the 10.

To play the ace of hearts next would cost the contract. East would ruff and declarer would end with five trump tricks, three heart tricks, and the diamond ace – one trick short. The youngster in fact called for dummy's ♡9. Since Robin Hood held two trumps to his partner's one at this stage, he could not gain by ruffing this trick. He discarded a club and declarer ruffed in his hand. Robert Gorsham then drew the outstanding trumps with the queen and ace, claiming the contract.

'Excellent, young Robert,' declared Alan A'Dale. 'You were very light for your overcall. That must be a near top for us.'

'You young rascal!' exclaimed Aegwyn. 'Give your poor mother a bottom score, would you, after all she's done for you?'

A few rounds later, Robin Hood shared a table with Maid Marian, Little John, and an ancient villager by the name of Wilhemina. With his beloved Marian sitting opposite, Hood picked up these cards:

♠ A 10 9 8 7 3
♡ Q J 4
♢ K 8 2
♣ Q

'One No-trump,' said Maid Marian. In the Nottingham Club system this showed 13-15 points.

The old crone in the East seat thumbed through her cards. 'No bid from me,' she declared.

'Four Spades,' said Robin Hood.

Little John passed and Hood gathered his concentration, ready to play the contract. However, it seemed that Maid Marian was considering a further call. 'Six Spades,' she said.

There was no further bidding. Little John led ♣10 and Hood awaited the dummy with some interest.

This was the full deal:

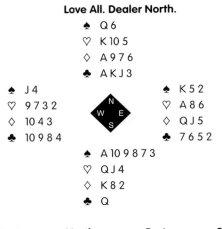

```
                    ♠ Q 6
                    ♡ K 10 5
                    ◇ A 9 7 6
                    ♣ A K J 3
  ♠ J 4                              ♠ K 5 2
  ♡ 9 7 3 2          N              ♡ A 8 6
  ◇ 10 4 3       W       E           ◇ Q J 5
  ♣ 10 9 8 4          S              ♣ 7 6 5 2
                    ♠ A 10 9 8 7 3
                    ♡ Q J 4
                    ◇ K 8 2
                    ♣ Q
```

West	North	East	South
Little	*Maid*	*Old*	*Robin*
John	*Marian*	*Wilhemina*	*Hood*
	1NT	Pass	4♠
Pass	6♠	All Pass	

'As you see, I have a queen extra for my bid,' announced Marian proudly. 'Since it is the queen of trumps, no less, I could hardly pass Four Spades.'

Hood gave a good-natured smile. 'No, indeed,' he replied.

The club lead was won by the queen in the South hand. Robin Hood then crossed to the ace of diamonds and played three more rounds of clubs, discarding all his hearts. 'King of hearts, please, Marian,' he said.

The ace appeared from East and Hood ruffed. Now, how could he return to dummy to take a discard on ♡10? It seemed he would need to lead towards the queen of trumps, hoping that West held the king.

Hood led the 3 of trumps from his hand and Little John followed unconcernedly with the 4. This was not what Hood had been hoping to see. Still, if Little John did hold the king he would surely have given some consideration to rising with it. 'Play the 6, please, Marian,' said Robin Hood.

With a cluck of annoyance at having to waste an honour on so lowly a card, Old Wilhemina won with the king. Hood took the diamond queen return with the king and crossed to dummy with the queen of trumps. He discarded his diamond loser on ♡10 and ruffed dummy's last heart to return to his hand. The last trump fell under declarer's ace and the slam had been made.

'Lead a heart!' cried Old Wilhemina. 'My ace wins and we must make a trump trick.'

Little John glared at the old woman. 'What, lead from four 'earts to the 9?' he exclaimed. 'I 'ad a sequence in clubs, four to the 1098.'

'Always lead the major when they've opened in no-trumps,' persisted the crone. 'See what happened on this hand and you can understand why.'

Little John might have beaten the contract in a different way, thought Robin Hood. Had he inserted the jack on the first round of trumps, he would have killed the extra entry to dummy.

The players rose to change partners for the second board of the round. Old Wilhemina would now partner the outlaw leader. Robin Hood could scarcely believe it as he picked up one of the finest hands he had ever held.

North/South Game. Dealer South.

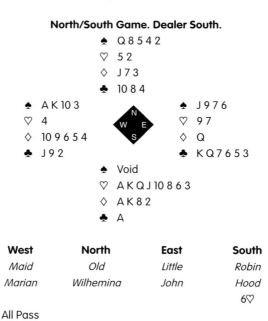

	♠	Q 8 5 4 2
	♡	5 2
	♢	J 7 3
	♣	10 8 4

West		East
♠ A K 10 3		♠ J 9 7 6
♡ 4		♡ 9 7
♢ 10 9 6 5 4		♢ Q
♣ J 9 2		♣ K Q 7 6 5 3

	♠	Void
	♡	A K Q J 10 8 6 3
	♢	A K 8 2
	♣	A

West	North	East	South
Maid	*Old*	*Little*	*Robin*
Marian	*Wilhemina*	*John*	*Hood*
			6♡

All Pass

It seemed to Robin Hood that there was no way to bid his hand scientifically, particularly with his present partner. His main aim should perhaps be to deter a cheap sacrifice in one of the black suits. 'Six Hearts,' he said.

Old Wilhemina leaned forwards. 'Speak up, young man,' she said. 'Did you say One Heart?'

'No, no,' intervened Maid Marian. 'Robin bid Six Hearts.'

The old woman's mouth fell open. An opening bid of Six Hearts? Ridiculous, she had never heard of such a call.

Neither defender doubled, Old Wilhemina was pleased to see, and Marian led the ace of spades. Robin Hood ruffed the first trick and saw he would have to make plans for his diamond losers. What if he drew trumps, cashed the diamond ace, and led a second round of diamonds towards the jack? He would succeed whenever West held the diamond queen, the queen fell singleton from East, or the suit broke 3-3.

How about playing a diamond to the jack before drawing trumps? Yes, that looked better. If the jack lost to East's queen, he could win the return, draw just one round of trumps, then play the two top diamonds. If the player with the outstanding trump also held four diamonds he would be able to ruff the fourth round of the suit.

'It's you to play,' said Old Wilhemina.

'Ah yes, thank you,' replied Robin Hood. He led a low diamond from his hand. 'Play the jack, will you?'

'A young man like you should play the cards 'imself,' declared Old Wilhemina. 'I 'ave a bad arm.'

Robin Hood reached for dummy's jack of diamonds. Little John won with the queen and returned the king of clubs, taken by South's ace. Following his plan, Robin Hood drew just one round of trumps, then attempted to cash the ace of diamonds. Little John ruffed and the contract was one down.

Old Wilhemina leaned forward in disgruntled fashion. 'I thought as much,' she exclaimed. 'Openin' with a Six bid? I ain't never 'eard such nonsense.'

'I had a good hand,' Hood replied.

'Not good enough, obviously,' continued the old woman. She opened the travelling score-sheet. 'Good gracious, everyone else has bid and made Six Hearts. Two pairs scored an overtrick!'

'Yes, it works well if I draw trumps,' replied Robin Hood. 'The queen of diamonds falls and West is squeezed in spades and diamonds.'

'Typical of my luck,' grumbled Old Wilhemina. 'You play like a champion when the pretty young thing is opposite. When my turn comes, you can't even remember to draw trumps.'

The last hand of the round put the two ladies together.

East/West Game. Dealer West.

```
                  ♠ A K 10 6
                  ♡ A 9 8 5 3
                  ◇ Q 7
                  ♣ A 3
   ♠ J                          ♠ 7 3 2
   ♡ K J 10 7 6 4 2       N     ♡ Void
   ◇ 8 6 4            W       E  ◇ J 9 5 3 2
   ♣ K Q                 S     ♣ J 10 8 5 2
                  ♠ Q 9 8 5 4
                  ♡ Q
                  ◇ A K 10
                  ♣ 9 7 6 4
```

West	North	East	South
Robin	*Old*	*Little*	*Maid*
Hood	*Wilhemina*	*John*	*Marian*
3♡	Dble	Pass	4♠
Pass	6♠	All Pass	

'The double of Three Hearts was for take-out?' enquired Robin Hood, who was on lead.

'Presumably,' replied Maid Marian. 'We hadn't discussed it.'

'Of course it weren't for take-out,' exclaimed Old Wilhemina. 'If you don't play penalty doubles, people start pre-emptin' on rubbish.'

Robin Hood led the king of clubs, Marian winning with dummy's ace. When she cashed the ace of trumps, the jack fell from West. Abandoning trumps for the moment, she played three rounds of diamonds. Both defenders followed and a club was thrown from the dummy. Marian ruffed one club, then paused to survey this position:

Wilhemina
♠ K 10
♡ A 9 8 5 3
♢ —
♣ —

Robin Hood
♠ —
♡ K J 10 7 6 4 2
♢ —
♣ —

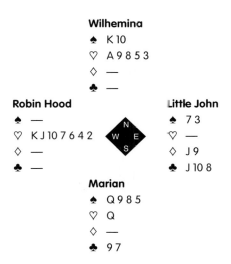

Little John
♠ 7 3
♡ —
♢ J 9
♣ J 10 8

Marian
♠ Q 9 8 5
♡ Q
♢ —
♣ 9 7

Declarer, who had not yet lost a trick, considered her next play carefully. If she called for the ace of hearts, there was every chance after West's pre-empt in the suit, that East would ruff. He would then be able to return a trump, leaving her one trick short. What could be done?

Marian soon spotted the answer. 'Small heart, please,' she said.

Little John, sitting East, was powerless. If he ruffed and returned a trump, declarer would be able to throw one club on the ace of hearts and ruff the other club. Little John in fact decided to throw a club on the trick. West won with the heart king and returned another heart. Declarer could now face her remaining cards, claiming the remainder on a high cross-ruff.

Old Wilhemina looked far from appreciative. 'He shouldn't make that king of 'earts, should he?' she queried. 'You wasted my ace.'

Robin Hood gave a rueful shake of the head. 'She made the fullest use possible of your ace, I think you'll find,' he said. 'Clever piece of play, Marian.'

Play continued enjoyably for two or three hours. The last round of the evening brought Hood together with Nazir and Friar Tuck. The table was completed by Ted Godwit, the swineherd.

On the first hand Robin Hood watched helplessly as the swineherd went two down vulnerable in a simple part-score contract. He smiled to himself. Everyone always expected him to win these individual events; in truth, there was a fair amount of luck involved.

Hood partnered Friar Tuck on the next deal.

North/South Game. Dealer South.

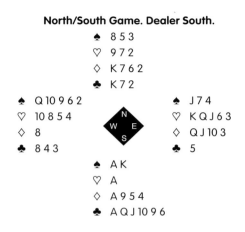

```
                    ♠ 8 5 3
                    ♡ 9 7 2
                    ◇ K 7 6 2
                    ♣ K 7 2
  ♠ Q 10 9 6 2                      ♠ J 7 4
  ♡ 10 8 5 4          N             ♡ K Q J 6 3
  ◇ 8             W       E         ◇ Q J 10 3
  ♣ 8 4 3             S             ♣ 5
                    ♠ A K
                    ♡ A
                    ◇ A 9 5 4
                    ♣ A Q J 10 9 6
```

West	North	East	South
Friar	*Ted*	*Robin*	*Nazir*
Tuck	*Godwit*	*Hood*	
			2◇
Pass	2♡	Dble	3♣
Pass	4♣	Pass	6♣
All Pass			

Nazir began with Two Diamonds, the strongest opening in the Nottingham Club system. North made the negative response of Two Hearts and Robin Hood doubled to suggest a strong holding in that suit. When the club fit came to light Nazir leapt straight to Six Clubs, ending the auction.

Holding four hearts himself, Friar Tuck could see little future in a heart lead. He led his singleton ◇8 and Hood contributed a mildly deceptive jack, Nazir winning with the ace. All seemed to depend on the lie of the diamond suit, thought Nazir. Could the Friar have led from such as ◇8-3 or ◇Q-10-8? Surely he wouldn't ignore his partner's call for a heart lead with either of those holdings. No, the diamond lead must be a singleton.

Nazir played the ace and queen of trumps, East showing out on the second round. He cashed his two spade honours and crossed to the king of clubs. He then ruffed a third round of spades, removing East's last spade in the process.

One more round of trumps left this end position:

Ted Godwit
- ♠ —
- ♡ 9 7
- ◇ K 7 6
- ♣ —

Friar Tuck
- ♠ Q 10
- ♡ 10 8 5
- ◇ —
- ♣ —

Robin Hood
- ♠ —
- ♡ K Q
- ◇ Q 10 3
- ♣ —

Nazir
- ♠ —
- ♡ A
- ◇ 9 5 4
- ♣ 10

Nazir now played his last trump, throwing a heart from the table. If Robin Hood were to throw a diamond, declarer would play king and another diamond, setting up a twelfth trick in the suit. Reluctantly, he had to throw the queen of hearts.

Nazir was certain how the cards lay. He cashed the ace of hearts, drawing Hood's last heart, and led a diamond towards dummy. When West showed out, he called for dummy's 7. Hood gave a respectful nod in Nazir's direction, as he won with the 10 and had to return a diamond from the queen. 'You played it well,' he said.

'Not difficult on that lead,' replied Nazir. 'A heart lead would beat it, I think.'

'Easy to say that now,' declared an affronted Friar Tuck. 'If there's a man in England who doesn't lead a singleton against a small slam, I've yet to meet him.'

Hood laughed. 'The fault lay in my double of Two Hearts,' he said. 'It wasn't loud enough, obviously.'

'Complete top for us, Nazir,' declared Ted Godwit, completing the travelling scoresheet in a laboured hand. 'No-one else was makin' it.'

The penultimate board of the tournament saw the outlaws' finest partnership in action. Robin Hood was North, with Nazir South.

Love All. Dealer South.

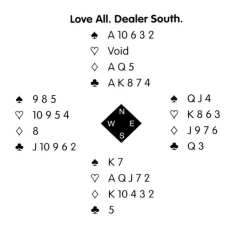

North hand:
♠ A 10 6 3 2
♡ Void
♢ A Q 5
♣ A K 8 7 4

West hand:
♠ 9 8 5
♡ 10 9 5 4
♢ 8
♣ J 10 9 6 2

East hand:
♠ Q J 4
♡ K 8 6 3
♢ J 9 7 6
♣ Q 3

South hand:
♠ K 7
♡ A Q J 7 2
♢ K 10 4 3 2
♣ 5

West	North	East	South
Friar	*Robin*	*Ted*	*Nazir*
Tuck	*Hood*	*Godwit*	
			1♡
Pass	1♠	Pass	2♢
Pass	3♣	Pass	3♢
Pass	6♢	All Pass	

'Three Clubs was natural, was it?' enquired Friar Tuck, who was on lead.

'Not necessarily,' replied Nazir. 'Robin and I have invented a special meaning for a call in the fourth suit. It just shows a strong hand.'

The Friar chuckled to himself. 'I hardly think the idea will catch on,' he said.

Friar Tuck led the jack of clubs and Nazir won with dummy's ace. If trumps were 3-2 the contract would be easy. He could ruff one heart, discard another, and concede just one trick to the king of hearts. 'Ace of trumps, please,' said Nazir.

All followed to the trump ace but West showed out when the queen of trumps was played. What could be done now? Changing tack, Nazir cashed the king and ace of spades and ruffed a spade. The suit divided 3-3 and he returned to dummy with a heart ruff. Nazir discarded a heart on the king of clubs, leaving these cards outstanding:

Robin Hood
♠ 10 6
♡ —
◇ —
♣ 8 7 4

Friar Tuck
♠ —
♡ 10 9
◇ —
♣ 10 9 6

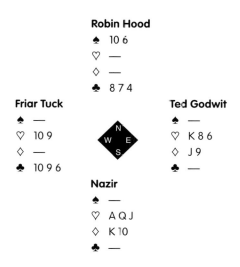

Ted Godwit
♠ —
♡ K 8 6
◇ J 9
♣ —

Nazir
♠ —
♡ A Q J
◇ K 10
♣ —

'Spade ten,' said Nazir.

East could not afford to let the two good spades win, since declarer would then easily score two of the remaining three tricks. He ruffed ♠10 with the ◇9, overruffed by declarer's ◇10. Nazir drew East's last trump and continued with the ace and queen of hearts. East won with the king and at trick 13 had to return a heart to declarer's jack. Despite the adverse trump break the slam had been made.

'Fine play, Nazir,' declared Robin Hood. 'Not that it will help my own position very much.'

The scoring of the event was traditionally entrusted to William the Cheesemaker now well into his eighties. Painstakingly meticulous with his calculations, he had been known to take over an hour to deliver the result.

A throng of villagers surrounded Robin Hood. 'How did you fare, Robin?' asked Henry Leadbetter, the head man of the village.

'About average, I think,' replied Robin Hood.

The crowd burst into laughter. 'That's what you said last year,' declared Leadbetter. 'You won by two clear tops, I remember.'

'No, no, this time I mean it,' protested Hood. 'You'll find out soon enough.'

Two large barrels of beer had been untapped and they were nearly drained by the time William the Cheesemaker emerged with the result sheets.

'Young Robert Gorsham were in third place,' he shouted. 'Very fine

The Michaelmas Individual

result, that be, for someone of just seventeen years.'

'Not true!' someone called out. 'He were eighteen last Tuesday.'

William the Cheesemaker glared at the heckler. 'Very well done, anyroad,' he said. 'And in second place were your favourite singer of ballads, Alan A' Dale.'

The crowd applauded then settled into an expectant hush, waiting to hear who had won the event.

'In first place, it were ... guess who?' cried William the Cheesemaker.

'Robin Hood!' shouted everyone in chorus. 'Robin Hood!'

William the Cheesemaker looked pleased with himself. 'No, he were well down the list,' he said. 'Just below me in fact.'

'Didn't I tell you?' said Robin Hood to those around him.

'In first place were that fine player, Nazir the Saracen,' announced William the Cheesemaker. 'Step forward, young man, to receive the first prize!'

8
THE LUCAS STREET PAIRS

'Is the court jester not better?' demanded the Sheriff. 'The evenings have been dull without his company.'

'No, my Lord,' replied Gisburne. 'The physicians have administered the cuts and the leeches, but no good has come from it.'

'I am surrounded by fools,' declared the Sheriff. 'A jester who cannot jest, physicians who cannot heal and ... a commander of the guard who cannot capture Robin Hood!'

'I hear the court minstrel has some amusing new songs, my Lord,' said Gisburne. 'Perhaps he could entertain us tonight.'

'His voice is as soothing as that of a woman in labour,' said the Sheriff. 'No, summon two tarts from Lucas Street. At least they are competent in their profession.'

'Tonight is the one night of the year when Lucas Street is closed, my Lord,' replied Gisburne. 'They are holding their annual pairs competition.'

'Are you serious?' said the Sheriff. 'Just for the women, is it, or do the customers compete too?'

'Both, my Lord,' replied Gisburne. 'But surely you don't suggest we should play in the event? Men of our stature could hardly be seen in such an environment.'

A glint came to the Sheriff's eye. 'The evilmongers of Sherwood evade attention by means of disguise,' he declared. 'It should not be beyond two Norman noblemen to do the same.'

That evening, at the appropriately late hour of nine, the Lucas Street Pairs commenced. The hovels of the district were small and most could accommodate only one card table. Gisburne and the Sheriff, who were dressed in commoners' garb borrowed from the Castle jailer, played their first round in the tiny bedroom of 17 Lucas Street.

'And who might you be?' said the Sheriff, studying the pretty young North player with obvious interest.

'Slippery Sue, I'm called 'ere,' she replied. 'Course, it ain't my real name.'

'What is your real name, my dear?' enquired the Sheriff.

'I were christened Gorlthrop,' replied the girl.

The Sheriff nodded sympathetically and turned to the occupant of the South seat. Good God, he thought, she couldn't be a day under fifty. How on earth did she make a living? 'And you?' he said.

'My name is Charlotte,' replied the woman. 'Shall we start?'

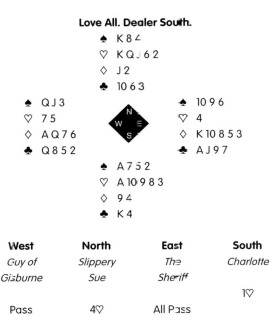

Love All. Dealer South.

```
                ♠ K 8 4
                ♡ K Q J 6 2
                ◊ J 2
                ♣ 10 6 3
  ♠ Q J 3                      ♠ 10 9 6
  ♡ 7 5            N           ♡ 4
  ◊ A Q 7 6     W     E        ◊ K 10 8 5 3
  ♣ Q 8 5 2        S           ♣ A J 9 7
                ♠ A 7 5 2
                ♡ A 10 9 8 3
                ◊ 9 4
                ♣ K 4
```

West	North	East	South
Guy of	*Slippery*	*The*	*Charlotte*
Gisburne	*Sue*	*Sheriff*	
			1♡
Pass	4♡	All Pass	

Gisburne led the queen of spades against Four Hearts and down went the dummy. The middle-aged declarer studied it impassively, giving no clue as to whether the contract was a good one. 'Play the 4,' she said.

The Sheriff followed with the 6 and declarer contributed a deceptive 7.

The Sheriff rarely showed approval of his partner's opening leads and a delighted Gisburne lost no time in continuing with the jack of spades. Declarer won with dummy's king, drew trumps in two rounds, and cashed two more spade winners, discarding a diamond from dummy. When the ace of clubs proved to be onside, she had ten tricks before her.

'Switch to a diamond or a club, you buffoon!' cried the Sheriff. 'We had four tricks to take off the top.'

'How could I read the situation?' replied Gisburne. 'Did you not see? The harlot, here, played the 7 on the first trick. I thought your 6 was an encouraging signal.'

'Harlot! How dare you?' cried the woman sitting South. 'I am Charlotte de Gryse, well known for my good works among these poor unfortunates.'

The Sheriff could not care less who the South player might be. 'You read me for A-6-5-2 in the spade suit?' he persisted. 'That would leave declarer with 10-9-7. She would have covered in the dummy, to make sure of a winner on the third round.'

'True, but you might have held A-10-6 or A-10-6-2,' observed Charlotte de Gryse. 'I wouldn't cover with dummy's king then.'

The Sheriff gazed at the strange woman in astonishment. Deceptive plays were rare enough, even among the stronger sex. She spoke about the game with authority too. It was quite unnatural.

The traditional Lucas Street movement was being used: the East-West pairs moving up one house, the cards down one house. The second round of the event saw the Sheriff and Gisburne in 19 Lucas Street. Sitting South, they were alarmed to find, was a dark-haired girl known professionally as Strict Megwyn. She had visited Nottingham Castle on more than one occasion and there was a fair chance she would see through their rather thin disguises.

The North player was Tom Graines, a 40-year-old patron of Strict Megwyn, who was sitting rather uncomfortably on his chair, continually changing his position.

This was the first hand they played:

Game All. Dealer East.

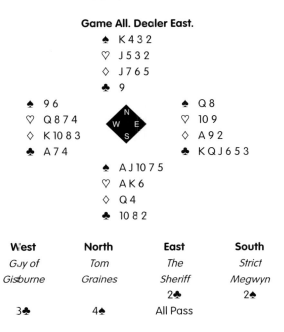

                    ♠ K 4 3 2
                    ♡ J 5 3 2
                    ◇ J 7 6 5
                    ♣ 9

  ♠ 9 6   ♠ Q 8
  ♡ Q 8 7 4   ♡ 10 9
  ◇ K 10 8 3   ◇ A 9 2
  ♣ A 7 4   ♣ K Q J 6 5 3

                    ♠ A J 10 7 5
                    ♡ A K 6
                    ◇ Q 4
                    ♣ 10 8 2

West	North	East	South
Guy of	*Tom*	*The*	*Strict*
Gisburne	*Graines*	*Sheriff*	*Megwyn*
		2♣	2♠
3♣	4♠	All Pass	

The Sheriff opened with a natural Two Clubs, denying the strength for a strong Nottingham club. Strict Megwyn overcalled Two Spades and Gisburne bid Three Clubs. Tom Graines raised to Four Spades and there was no further bidding.

Gisburne led the ace of clubs and switched to a trump after a brief inspection of the dummy. Hoping to establish a diamond trick on which to throw her heart loser, Megwyn won the trump switch with dummy's king and led a diamond. The queen lost to West's king and Gisburne returned another trump. Declarer won in the South hand and ducked a second round of diamonds to East's 9. Winning the ♡10 switch with the ace, she ruffed a club in dummy. A diamond ruff then brought down East's ace, setting up dummy's jack. A second club ruff gave entry to the dummy and Megwyn threw her heart loser on the established diamond. 'There we are, Tom,' she said, flashing a splendid smile at her partner. 'Ten tricks for you.'

Her partner seemed less than overjoyed that the game had been made. 'I thought my Four Spade bid might merit some ... er ... reprimand,' he replied. 'It's not the first time I've overbid.'

Strict Megwyn laughed. 'All in good time, my love,' she said.

The Sheriff could not hide his exasperation. 'Why on earth didn't you play another club, partner?' he cried. 'One more club lead would kill the entry to the diamond winner. You were on lead twice.'

Gisburne was beginning to regret the decision to play in the event. 'I thought by playing on trumps I might stop her ruffing clubs in the dummy,' he replied.

'You wanted to stop club ruffs?' exclaimed the Sheriff. 'You buffoon! Forcing the dummy to ruff was the only way to beat the contract.'

Megwyn turned towards the Sheriff. 'Don't be nasty to 'im,' she said. 'Everyone makes a bit of a Gisburne now and again.'

The Sheriff stopped in his tracks. 'What did you say?' he enquired.

'You know, a bit of a cock-up,' replied Megwyn. 'We calls it a Gisburne around 'ere. After that clown in the Castle.'

The Sheriff sucked in his cheeks, staring exultantly across the table. 'Have you heard that expression before, partner?' he said. 'I must add it to my vocabulary. No doubt it arises from the man's persistent failure to capture Robin Hood.'

Seeking to retrieve something from the situation, Gisburne turned towards the dark-haired declarer. 'Perhaps you know some of the outlaws,' he said. 'Do they ever come to Lucas Street?'

'Good 'eavens, no,' replied Megwyn, laughing. 'Men like that don't need to pay for it.'

Suddenly she realised her gaffe. 'Not that there's anythin' wrong with men what do pay, of course,' she added. 'You're very 'andsome, all three of you.'

A round or two later the Sheriff and Gisburne found themselves in 23 Lucas Street. The oil lamps provided enough light to view the cards but rain was leaking through roof in several places.

'Surely the owner of this house can afford to have the roof mended,' declared the Sheriff, shaking some water off the cards he had just picked up. 'You girls charge enough, I should know.'

'Poor Mandy lives in this one,' replied Bendy Brenda, a pretty girl with short fair hair. 'She don't make much money since she caught the plague.'

'Hope we don't catch nuffink off the chairs,' said the ruby-lipped girl sitting North. She was known on the street as 'French' Laura, despite having a strong Newcastle accent. 'You to bid, Bendy.'

North/South Game. Dealer South.

```
              ♠ 6 5
              ♡ K 7 2
              ◇ A J 9 8 2
              ♣ 8 5 2
   ♠ 9 3                        ♠ K 10 8 7 4
   ♡ 10 8          N            ♡ J 9 6 5 3
   ◇ Q 7 6 4    W     E         ♣ 10 5
   ♣ Q J 10 9 3    S            ♣ 6
              ♠ A Q J 2
              ♡ A Q 4
              ◇ K 3
              ♣ A K 7 4
```

West	North	East	South
Guy of	*French*	*The*	*Bendy*
Gisburne	*Laura*	*Sheriff*	*Brenda*
			2◇
Pass	3◇	Pass	3NT
Pass	6NT	All Pass	

South made the strongest opening in the Nottingham Club system and soon reached 6NT. Gisburne led the queen of clubs and she won with the king. The young declarer had not played bridge for long. Indeed her only instruction with regard to card-play had been on how to take a finesse. She remembered vaguely some other rule about always drawing trumps straight away. Still, presumably that didn't apply when there weren't any trumps. Finesses it would have to be.

At trick two Bendy Brenda led ◇3. 'Finesse the jack, will you?' she said

The young declarer's eyes shone triumphantly when the jack won the trick. These finesses were great – extra tricks out of thin air! What should she do next? Not much point in finessing the queen of hearts when the king was in dummy. 'Play one of them spades,' she said.

A finesse of the spade queen proved successful but the young declarer seemed at a loss what to do next. Even if she made three spades, three hearts and two clubs, she would still need several tricks from the diamond suit. Yes, better do something there.

Bendy Brenda led the king of diamonds, overtaking with the ace. When ◇10 fell from East, declarer resisted the temptation to take another spade finesse, preferring to set up the diamond suit instead. Gisburne won the third round of diamonds with the queen and cleared the club suit, but the contract was now secure. Declarer cashed three rounds of hearts, ending in the dummy, then finessed the jack of spades. Twelve tricks were before her.

'About time, I say,' observed French Laura. 'First contract we've made all evenin'.'

'Ain't my fault, Laura,' retorted Bendy Brenda. 'You've gone down more times than me.'

This was the next hand:

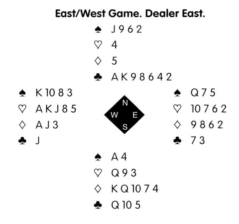

East/West Game. Dealer East.

	♠ J 9 6 2	
	♡ 4	
	◇ 5	
	♣ A K 9 8 6 4 2	
♠ K 10 8 3		♠ Q 7 5
♡ A K J 8 5		♡ 10 7 6 2
◇ A J 3		◇ 9 8 6 2
♣ J		♣ 7 3
	♠ A 4	
	♡ Q 9 3	
	◇ K Q 10 7 4	
	♣ Q 10 5	

West	North	East	South
Guy of	*French*	*The*	*Bendy*
Gisburne	*Laura*	*Sheriff*	*Brenda*
		Pass	1NT
Dble	3NT	All Pass	

Gisburne made a penalty double of 1NT and was amazed to find the Newcastle girl raising to 3NT. Seeing no reason to double, he passed the bid out and led the ace of hearts.

Gisburne watched closely the spot-cards that appeared on the first trick: the 4, 2 and 3. The Sheriff would surely have signalled with a higher card than the 2 if he held the heart queen, thought Gisburne. So, how could the contract be beaten? South's bid had promised 13-15 points, so East was marked with at most a queen.

Suddenly inspiration struck. Perhaps the Sheriff held the queen of spades! Yes, if he were to switch to the spade king now, declarer might capture immediately, placing him with the king-queen. It would then be possible to cross to the Sheriff's queen for a heart return.

Hoping for the best, Gisburne placed the king of spades on the table. The Sheriff signalled encouragement with the 7 and Bendy Brenda won with the ace. The run of the club suit caused Gisburne no problem; he threw two spades, two hearts and two diamonds. When the young declarer played a diamond to her king, Gisburne won with the ace and crossed to the Sheriff's queen of spades for a heart through. The game was one down.

'What you raisin' to 3NT for?' complained Bendy Brenda. 'I'd 'ave made 1NT doubled.'

'They wouldn't leave it in 1NT,' replied French Laura. 'I 'ad seven clubs. It were obvious the next player would 'ave a long suit somewhere.'

Pleased to have achieved a good board at last the Sheriff displayed his cards to the two girls. 'Not so, as it happens,' he said. 'With a 4-4-3-2 shape I would have left the double in.'

Gisburne could not believe it. After such a magnificent defence how could everyone be discussing the bidding? 'My king of spades worked well,' he observed. 'There should be a special name for a play like that.'

It was still raining heavily as the Sheriff and Gisburne walked towards 4 Lucas Street for the last round. A surprisingly plush establishment, this was the home of Loose Lillian, the queen of Lucas Street. The four chairs around the bridge table were each graced by an embroidered cushion; there were even curtains at the window. As befitted her high standing in the community, Loose Lillian had been assigned a stationary position in her own house.

'Wipe your feet!' cried the henna-haired Loose Lillian, as the Sheriff and Gisburne came through the front door. 'Don't want my carpet gettin' all muddy.'

Not overpleased at being ordered around by a mere tart, the Sheriff wiped his boots and took the East seat.

'Can't say I recognise you two gents,' observed Loose Lillian. 'You know 'em, Betsy?'

The occupant of the North seat, known locally as Big Betsy studied Gisburne closely. 'Someone a bit similar-lookin' used to come down 'ere of a night-time,' she replied. 'But 'e were posher, wore finer clothes.'

Loose Lillian turned towards Gisburne. 'You know our Betsy?' she enquired.

'No, no,' replied Gisburne. 'We've ... er ... never met.'

The Sheriff viewed Gisburne's discomfort with some amusement. So, the great Sir Guy patronised Lucas Street, did he? That would be an amusing story to pass around at court.

'Shy sort of man, the other one was,' continued Big Betsy. 'Wouldn't never take 'is clothes off until I made the room really dark.'

Better and better, thought the Sheriff. Lady Marguerite de Boeuf would be particularly entertained to hear of it.

The required boards were eventually transported from the next hut and the final round of the Lucas Street Pairs began.

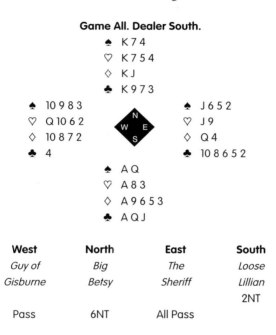

Game All. Dealer South.

	♠ K 7 4	
	♡ K 7 5 4	
	◇ K J	
	♣ K 9 7 3	
♠ 10 9 8 3		♠ J 6 5 2
♡ Q 10 6 2		♡ J 9
◇ 10 8 7 2		◇ Q 4
♣ 4		♣ 10 8 6 5 2
	♠ A Q	
	♡ A 8 3	
	◇ A 9 6 5 3	
	♣ A Q J	

West	North	East	South
Guy of	*Big*	*The*	*Loose*
Gisburne	*Betsy*	*Sheriff*	*Lillian*
			2NT
Pass	6NT	All Pass	

Gisburne led ♠10 against 6NT. The Sheriff signalled encouragement with the 6 and declarer won with the ace. The blockage in the two black suits somewhat restricted declarer's mobility. She cashed the spade queen followed by her three club honours, Gisburne throwing two spades. A diamond to the jack lost to East's queen and the Sheriff spent some time considering his return. It was easy enough to lead passively to one of the table's three bare kings, but he saw that a heart return might prove more awkward for declarer. There was an evident risk that a red-suit squeeze would develop against Gisburne; a heart return might remove a key entry in that suit.

Loose Lillian was not pleased to see the jack of hearts appear on the table. After some thought she won the trick with dummy's king. On the king of spades she threw a diamond and Gisburne discarded a heart.

These cards remained:

Betsy
♠ —
♡ 7 5 4
◊ K
♣ K

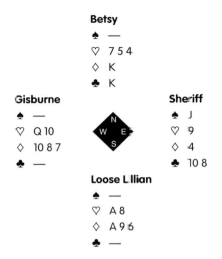

Gisburne
♠ —
♡ Q 10
◊ 10 8 7
♣ —

Sheriff
♠ J
♡ 9
◊ 4
♣ 10 8

Loose Lillian
♠ —
♡ A 8
◊ A 9 6
♣ —

'King of clubs, Betsy,' said Loose Lillian, discarding ♡8 from her hand.

Gisburne had no good card to play. If he threw a diamond, declarer would cash the diamond king and cross to the ace of hearts to claim the last two diamonds. He eventually discarded a heart but now Loose Lillian crossed to the ace of hearts and returned to the diamond king. The ace of diamonds never scored a trick but dummy's 7 and 5 of hearts brought her total to twelve.

'Ain't never seen a play like that before!' exclaimed a delighted Loose Lillian.

The Sheriff blinked. How was it possible for a gap-toothed old tart to stumble into a squeeze like that? Perhaps she had special powers. Good God, she might even be a witch.

The players now drew their cards for the last hand of the evening:

North/South Game. Dealer East.

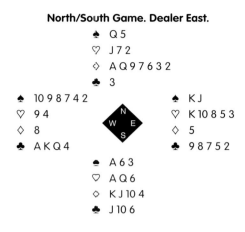

                    ♠ Q 5
                    ♡ J 7 2
                    ◇ A Q 9 7 6 3 2
                    ♣ 3

    ♠ 10 9 8 7 4 2   ♠ K J
    ♡ 9 4   ♡ K 10 8 5 3
    ◇ 8   ◇ 5
    ♣ A K Q 4   ♣ 9 8 7 5 2

                    ♠ A 6 3
                    ♡ A Q 6
                    ◇ K J 10 4
                    ♣ J 10 6

West	North	East	South
Guy of	*Big*	*The*	*Loose*
Gisburne	*Betsy*	*Sheriff*	*Lillian*
		Pass	1◇
1♠	5◇	All Pass	

Loose Lillian arrived in Five Diamonds after a brief auction and Gisburne led the ace of clubs. The Sheriff eyed the dummy approvingly. Gisburne's overcall marked him with the spade ace. He could hardly hold eight cards in the suit, so the ace and king were sure to stand up.

Pausing to make sure that he had Gisburne's full attention, the Sheriff slid the nine of clubs forward. This was a suit preference signal, requesting a spade switch. The message was not lost on Gisburne, who switched promptly to ♠10.

Loose Lillian was somewhat surprised to see this card. Could West be leading from the spade king? There seemed no reason for him to do so. He had a perfectly safe exit in clubs; maybe in trumps, too, if he had any. And what was to be made of this emphasized signal of the club nine? It was beginning to look as if it was East who held the spade king. 'Play the five,' said Loose Lillian.

The Sheriff contributed the jack of spades and declarer won with the ace. She proceeded to ruff a club, return to hand with a trump, and ruff her last club.

The lead was in dummy and these cards remained:

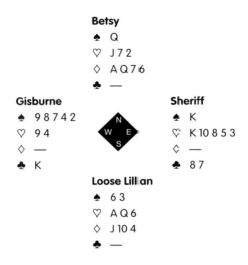

Betsy
- ♠ Q
- ♡ J 7 2
- ◇ A Q 7 6
- ♣ —

Gisburne
- ♠ 9 8 7 4 2
- ♡ 9 4
- ◇ —
- ♣ K

Sheriff
- ♠ K
- ♡ K 10 8 5 3
- ◇ —
- ♣ 8 7

Loose Lillian
- ♠ 6 3
- ♡ A Q 6
- ◇ J 10 4
- ♣ —

'Queen of spades, Betsy,' said Loose Lillian.

The Sheriff won with the bare king and was endplayed. He exited with a low heart, hoping to find his partner with an honour in the suit, but Gisburne could produce only the 9. Dummy's jack of hearts won the trick and a subsequent finesse of the heart queen brought home the contract.

'Disastrous spade switch, partner,' exclaimed the Sheriff. 'Exit passively and, after your overcall, declarer will play a spade to the queen.'

'But, but ... your nine of clubs,' stammered Gisburne. 'Surely that was the clearest of requests for a spade switch?'

'I thought you had the spade ace, you buffoon!' cried the Sheriff. 'No-one in his right mind would overcall on a ten-high suit.'

Play had finished at most of the other tables. More and more players were crowding into Loose Lillian's house, listening to the post-mortem with great amusement.

'It is too much, the way you blame me for every bad board,' Gisburne declared. 'I've had enough, my Lord. You will have to find another partner.'

A hush fell upon the crowd at the words 'my Lord'. Loose Lillian leaned forward, peering closely at the two intruders. 'Do you know who these two gents is, girls?' she said. 'Unless I be very much mistaken, it's none other than the Sheriff of Nottingham and Sir Guy of Gisburne!'

There were angry mutterings around the room. 'Ain't right,' said Slippery Sue. 'This is our special event. It's only once a year, they shouldn't be 'ere.'

The Sheriff looked desperately for a way of escape but the room was now packed to overflowing.

'Well, what do you think, girls?' said Loose Lillian, a mischievous glint in her eye. 'Men what comes to Lucas Street usually comes for one particular reason, don't they? They comes to 'ave a good time.'

'Let's take their clothes off!' shouted a red-headed girl at the back of the room. 'I'll give 'em a good time all right.'

The Sheriff rose to his feet in alarm. 'Don't you lay one finger on me!' he cried.

'Nor on me,' said Gisburne. 'You heard what his Lordship said.'

The will of Lucas Street could not be denied. The girls surged forward and Gisburne and the Sheriff were buried in a heaving mass of female bodies. One by one the various garments of their attire were tossed into the air, grabbed as souvenirs by the baying crowd.

Loose Lillian stood watching the spectacle, her hands ecstatically aloft. 'That's it, girls, make the most of it!' she cackled. 'They won't never be comin' to Lucas Street again, you can be sure of that.'

9
THE ONE-EYED MAN

All messages for the outlaws were delivered to the Drunken Pheasant alehouse. Three or four times a week the Landlord's eldest son would bring them to the camp in Sherwood.

'Anything interesting in the mail today?' asked Friar Tuck, one blustery April morning.

'No, mainly bills,' replied Robin Hood. 'How can we owe three shillings and eightpence to the baker? Do we really eat so much bread in a week?'

Friar Tuck gave a small cough. 'It's not only bread,' he said. 'He sends the odd few cakes and buns, I believe.'

'Does he now?' said Robin Hood, looking quizzically at the priest. 'I wonder who orders those.'

'What's that sealed message scroll, there?' enquired Friar Tuck, anxious to change the subject.

Hood broke the seal, raising an eyebrow as he read the scroll's contents. 'It's a challenge to a 40-board team-of-four match from someone called Benson of Bradford,' he said. 'Each side is to put up a purse of 100 pounds in gold, winners to take all.'

'That will be One-Eye Benson,' replied Tuck. 'Bunch of highwaymen, his lot. They were behind that kidnapping on the York road last year.'

'Still, such a sum in gold is not to be sneezed at,' declared Hood. 'I don't think they could touch us over 40 boards.'

Some two weeks later the teams met at a half-way venue, a travellers' rest house just outside Sheffield.

'Forty boards, then?' said Benson. He had lost an eye in a prison brawl a few years before. Various glass eyes had proved unsatisfactory and the socket was currently unoccupied. 'Is that agreed?'

'Yes,' replied Robin Hood. 'Five 8-board segments?'

'We always play 10-board segments down our way,' declared Benson. 'Make it four lots of 10.'

Hood and Nazir took their seats against Benson and his partner, the black-bearded Luke Grieve. 'You take boards 6 to 10,' said Benson to one of the ruffians who formed his other partnership. 'We'll start with 1 to 5 here.'

The opponents had provided the duplicate boards; they were the latest style, fashioned out of deerskin. The first five hands were soon dealt and play began.

Board 1. Love All. Dealer South.

♠ K J 6 3
♡ A Q J 8
◇ Q J 7 6
♣ 3

♠ 10 8 5 4
♡ Void
◇ A 9 5 3 2
♣ Q J 10 7

♠ A 9
♡ 10 6 5 3 2
◇ K 8 4
♣ 9 6 5

♠ Q 7 3
♡ K 9 7 4
◇ 10
♣ A K 8 4 2

West	North	East	South
Robin	*Luke*	*Nazir*	*One-Eye*
Hood	*Grieve*		*Benson*
			1♣
Pass	1◇	Pass	1♡
Pass	4♡	All Pass	

Robin Hood led the queen of clubs against Four Hearts, Benson winning with the ace. The diamond 10 ran to Nazir's king and he was quick to return a trump. West showed out and the trick was won by dummy's 8. Muttering an oath at the 5-0 trump break, Benson ruffed a diamond and played a spade to the king and ace. When Nazir returned another trump, declarer won in the dummy and ruffed a diamond with his remaining trump. Dummy's last diamond was discarded on the king of clubs and declarer now needed two more spaces to stand up. It was not to be. Nazir ruffed the third round of spades and the contract was one down.

'You went off?' exclaimed Grieve, looking none too pleased.

'Trumps was 5-0,' replied Benson. 'Didn't have no chance.'

Robin Hood and Nazir shared a glance. The contract should surely have been made. When declarer won the first round of trumps in dummy he should have run the queen of diamonds. No matter that this would lose to the ace; declarer would now score one spade, one diamond, two clubs, four trumps in dummy and two ruffs in the South hand. East's five trumps would amount to nothing.

The outlaw pair fared well enough on the next few boards, then something very strange happened.

Board 5. North/South Game. Dealer West.

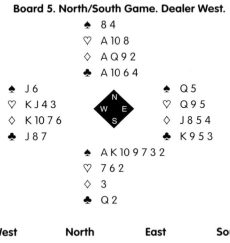

West	**North**	**East**	**South**
Robin	*Luke*	*Nazir*	*One-Eye*
Hood	*Grieve*		*Benson*
Pass	1NT	Pass	6♠
All Pass			

Robin Hood led ♡3 and down went the dummy. One-Eye Benson stared at it in apparent disbelief. 'You gone mad, Luke?' he cried. 'Only 14 points?'

'What do you expect when I open 1NT?' retorted his partner.

'You only bid 1NT?' exclaimed Benson. 'I 'eard 2NT.'

Robin Hood was well pleased at this turn of events. 'The contract is Six Spades, gentlemen,' he said. 'Shall we continue the play?'

Benson played low in the dummy and Nazir won the first trick with the queen of hearts. A heart continuation went to West's jack and the dummy's ace. 'Play the ace of clubs,' said One-Eye Benson.

Two rounds of trumps felled the defenders' holdings and declarer ran the remaining trumps. This end position arose:

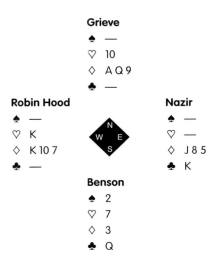

Grieve
♠ —
♡ 10
♢ A Q 9
♣ —

Robin Hood
♠ —
♡ K
♢ K 10 7
♣ —

Nazir
♠ —
♡ —
♢ J 8 5
♣ K

Benson
♠ 2
♡ 7
♢ 3
♣ Q

When the last trump was led, Robin Hood had to discard a diamond to retain his guard against dummy's ♡10. The heart was thrown from dummy and Nazir found himself in a similar position. To keep a guard against declarer's club queen, he too had to discard a diamond. One-Eye Benson finessed the queen of diamonds successfully and then cashed the ace of diamonds, both defenders following. 'What good boys!' he exclaimed. 'Unless I'm more mistaken than I've been in a long while, that nine of diamonds is good.'

Nazir shook his head in annoyance. 'Diamond return at trick 2 breaks the squeeze,' he said. 'Sorry.'

Robin Hood gazed curiously at the one-eyed declarer. How could someone who had misplayed a fairly simple hand only a few moments before suddenly make a hand like this? Hood's eyes narrowed. Even more astounding, of course, how had they managed to reach Six Spades on such limited values? As for that story about mis-hearing the opening bid, he didn't believe it for a moment.

Little John and Friar Tuck soon returned to score the first set. 'We did fairly well,' reported Friar Tuck. 'Except on Hand 10. I couldn't believe it, they bid 3NT on a combined 21-count and there was no way to beat it. Three suits lay favourably.'

'Luck of the devil!' exclaimed Robin Hood. 'We passed the board out.'

As a result of these two strange boards the outlaws found themselves 23 IMPs behind. Robin Hood and Nazir had a few promising boards at the start of the second set, then Hood found himself in 3NT.

Board 15. North/South Game. Dealer South.

```
                    ♠ Q 5 3
                    ♡ 9 8 6 4
                    ◇ A K 4
                    ♣ A 6 2
     ♠ K J 9 2                      ♠ A 7 4
     ♡ K 3 2            N           ♡ J 10 7 5
     ◇ 10 8 2       W     E         ◇ 9 7 5
     ♣ 9 7 4            S           ♣ J 10 5
                    ♠ 10 8 6
                    ♡ A Q
                    ◇ Q J 6 3
                    ♣ K Q 8 3
```

West	North	East	South
'Knifeman'	Nazir	Will	Robin
Hewett		McCreath	Hood
			1NT
Pass	3NT	All Pass	

Hewett, whose lower jaw was disfigured by an ugly scar, led the jack of spades against 3NT. Robin Hood surveyed Nazir's dummy for a few seconds. 'Play the queen,' he said.

McCreath won with the ace and returned a spade. West cashed three more tricks in the suit, the last of which put Hood to an awkward discard. What should he throw, he wondered, the queen of hearts or one of his clubs? Since a successful finesse in hearts was a better prospect than a 3-3 club break, he decided to throw a club. An eventual heart finesse failed and the contract was one down.

Hood eyed the West player suspiciously. 'That was a remarkable opening lead to find,' he declared.

'Always lead the jack from a broken sequence like that,' replied Hewett. 'Surprisin' how often it works.'

'It was an annoying lead, that's for sure,' observed Hood. 'After any other start I can test the clubs before falling back on the heart finesse.'

Meanwhile, at the far side of the room, Friar Tuck had just arrived in a vulnerable slam.

Board 20. Game All. Dealer West.

```
                    ♠  5
                    ♡  Q 10 9 8 6 4 2
                    ◊  Void
                    ♣  J 9 8 7 2
    ♠  A Q J 8 6                      ♠  K 10 9 7 3
    ♡  5                              ♡  A
    ◊  K 10 5 3          N            ◊  A 6
    ♣  Q 10 5        W     E          ♣  A K 6 4 3
                        S
                    ♠  4 2
                    ♡  K J 7 3
                    ◊  Q J 9 8 7 4 2
                    ♣  Void
```

West	North	East	South
Friar	*Luke*	*Little*	*One-Eye*
Tuck	*Grieve*	*John*	*Benson*
1♠	Pass	4NT	Pass
5◊	Pass	5NT	Pass
6◊	Pass	6♠	Dble
All Pass			

The outlaw pair reached Six Spades, doubled by Benson in the South seat. Grieve led ♣2 and Friar Tuck winced as this was ruffed by South. Still, the rest of the tricks should be there, thought the Friar; it was lucky they had not bid the grand.

Benson switched to the jack of diamonds, ruffed by his partner, and another club ruff by South put the slam two down doubled.

'Ow did you find that double?' demanded Little John, leaning threateningly towards One-Eye Benson.

'Well, lead-directin', weren't it?' replied Benson. 'I 'ad a void in dummy's first-bid suit.'

'Rubbish, I never bid my clubs,' declared Little John. 'I went straight for the Richmond ace-ask.'

Friar Tuck turned towards the bearded Grieve in the North seat. 'I don't understand how you found that club lead,' he said. 'You had seven hearts and only five clubs, didn't you?'

Grieve sniggered. 'Bit of a toss-up,' he replied. 'Just 'appened to lead the right suit.'

The next comparison went disastrously for the outlaw team. On Board

The One-Eyed Man

15 the highwaymen had easily made 3NT. On Board 20, the slam hand where Friar Tuck had suffered a defensive cross-ruff, McCreath had taken a conservative view of his 19-count, raising One Spade to Four Spades. The outlaws found they were now a serious 44 IMPs adrift.

'There's a funny smell about this,' said Robin Hood. 'We seem to play the better bridge but they keep getting these freak good boards.'

Nazir looked down at his scorecard. 'One thing is very strange,' he observed. 'The four big swings against us were on boards 5, 10, 15 and 20.'

'Peculiar, indeed,' said Hood. 'I wonder if...'

Nazir's thoughts were running in the same direction as his leader's. 'Maybe they have set a pre-arranged hand in every fifth board,' he said. 'Somehow they are not being redealt.'

'That's it!' exclaimed Hood. 'The stack of five boards is put on the table and we take one each to deal. The fifth board is taken by whoever deals the quickest.'

'Yes, yes,' said Nazir. 'They make sure it is one of them and perhaps switch the fifth board with one already dealt and redeal that one.'

'Cheatin' varmints!' exclaimed Little John. 'I'll murder 'em if that's true.'

'We will watch the deal closely in the next set and take whatever countermeasures occur to us,' said Robin Hood. 'Right, here they come.'

It was as Hood and Nazir had suspected. Benson dealt hand 21 with unusual speed, finishing first, then reached for hand 25. Almost in the blink of an eye he switched the two boards and began dealing board 21 again.

Play restarted and Hood and Nazir fared well on the first few hands. The tension tightened as board 25 was placed on the table. Hood extracted his own cards, a featureless 3-count. No doubt Benson was about to play the hand in some cleverly concocted slam contract. Under cover of the table Hood detached one of his cards, tucked it into his boot, and stretched out his leg towards Nazir. With barely a glance downwards, Nazir grasped what was happening. He reached for the card and added it to his own hand.

'Something wrong here,' declared Robin Hood. 'I have only twelve cards.'

'What?' cried an alarmed Benson. 'It ain't possible.'

Hood counted his cards onto the table. 'Only twelve,' he said.

'You dozy idiot!' exclaimed Benson. 'You must have dropped one.'

'No, no, it is a mis-deal,' said Nazir, counting out his own cards. 'Look, I have fourteen.'

To the highwaymen's obvious annoyance, the hand had to be re-dealt. The cards now lay like this:

Board 25. East/West Game. Dealer East.

```
              ♠ 10 7 4
              ♡ K J 9 5 2
              ◇ A K 8 3
              ♣ A
   ♠ J 8                    ♠ Q 9 3
   ♡ 10 8 4      N          ♡ A Q
   ◇ J 9 6 5   W   E        ◇ Q 7 4
   ♣ 7 6 4 2     S          ♣ K Q 10 8 5
              ♠ A K 6 5 2
              ♡ 7 6 3
              ◇ 10 2
              ♣ J 9 3
```

West	North	East	South
One-Eye	*Nazir*	*Luke*	*Robin*
Benson		*Grieve*	*Hood*
		1♣	1♠
Pass	4♠	All Pass	

A club was led against Four Spades, dummy's bare ace winning the trick. It seemed natural to play for two club ruffs but Hood saw that he was likely to lose control if he followed such a course. A better idea was to attempt to set up the hearts, while the trumps in dummy protected him from further club leads. The odds were good that East would hold ace doubleton in hearts. Even if this were not the case and declarer lost two tricks and a ruff in the heart suit, it would not necessarily be fatal. The ruff might come from a three-card trump holding.

'Small heart, please,' said Robin Hood.

The trick was taken by East's queen, Grieve switching to a trump. Hood won with the ace and played a second round of hearts, dummy's nine forcing the ace. A second round of trumps was won with the king and Hood was now in full control. His two club losers could be discarded on dummy's long hearts and the trump queen was the defenders' third and last trick.

'What happened to the fifth-dealt board at your table, board 30?' asked Robin Hood, when the outlaws met to score the third set. 'It was a gentle 1NT contract by the time it reached us.'

'No problem,' laughed Friar Tuck. 'I was very slow to take a board to deal. When the other three had each taken one, I reached underneath for board 30 and dealt that!'

The outlaws had recovered 19 IMPs but were still 25 IMPs adrift. 'Tell them we are in need of refreshment before the final set,' said Robin Hood. 'I have a plan. I will be back soon.'

The rest-house was well known for its home-smoked ham. Friar Tuck had almost cleared his second plateful by the time Hood returned. 'I have replaced boards 35 and 40,' he whispered. 'Allow them to pass undealt and the match is ours. Nazir, carry the bidding to Six Spades on board 40.'

Play restarted and after a few nondescript contracts at Robin Hood's table the players extracted their cards for board 35. Hood stole a glance at One-Eye Benson, who was sorting his cards in some disbelief. Yes, my friend, he thought. Not exactly the hand that you were expecting, is it?

Robin Hood, first to speak at favourable vulnerability, sorted through his own cards:

♠ 10 5 2
♡ J 10 8
♢ A 5 3
♣ J 10 9 2

He would not normally open the bidding on such values but, well, the intermediates were strong. 'One Spade,' said Robin Hood.

'One No-trump,' said One-Eye Benson.

Nazir passed and Luke Grieve raised to the no-trump game.

'Double,' said Robin Hood.

After two passes Grieve completed the auction with a redouble. This was the full deal:

Board 35. East/West Game. Dealer South.

```
              ♠  Void
              ♡  9 5 4 2
              ◇  Q 10 9 7 6 2
              ♣  7 6 4
♠ A Q J 6 3           N            ♠  K 9 8 7 4
♡ A Q 3          W         E        ♡  K 7 6
◇ J 8 4              S            ◇  K
♣ A 3                              ♣  K Q 8 5
              ♠  10 5 2
              ♡  J 10 8
              ◇  A 5 3
              ♣  J 10 9 2
```

West	North	East	South
One-Eye	Nazir	Luke	Robin
Benson		Grieve	Hood
			1♠
1NT	Pass	3NT	Dble
Pass	Pass	Rdble	All Pass

Nazir had no idea what trickery Hood had in mind, but surely he was intended to make the natural lead of a diamond. The diamond ten was covered by the king and ace. A diamond return through declarer's jack allowed the defenders to take the first six tricks and a score of +1000 went to North-South.

Benson glared evilly towards Hood. 'What in the Devil's name was this One Spade opening on three to the 10?' he cried. 'We were cold for Six Spades!'

Hood looked back innocently. 'You've outplayed us up till now,' he replied. 'A desperate measure was needed to get us back into the match.'

Hood and Nazir played soundly on the next four hands, then the final board of the match was placed on the table.

The One-Eyed Man

Board 40. Love All. Dealer East.

```
                    ♠ A 9 5 3
                    ♡ A K Q 8 6 3
                    ◇ Void
                    ♣ A 7 4
        ♠ Q                        ♠ K 10 6
        ♡ 10 9 5 2          N      ♡ J 4
        ◇ 7 6 2          W     E   ◇ A K J 9 4 3
        ♣ J 10 9 6 2        S      ♣ K Q
                    ♠ J 8 7 4 2
                    ♡ 7
                    ◇ Q 10 8 5
                    ♣ 8 5 3
```

West	North	East	South
One-Eye	Nazir	Luke	Robin
Benson		Grieve	Hood
		1◇	Pass
Pass	Dble	2◇	2♠
3◇	6♠	All Pass	

The outlaw pair arrived safely in the intended contract of Six Spades. Luke Grieve looked somewhat surprised to see them climb so high but opted not to double the final contract. The jack of clubs was led and Robin Hood won with dummy's ace, the queen coming from East. Both defenders followed to the ace and king of hearts, declarer discarding one of his club losers. 'Queen of hearts, please,' said Robin Hood.

Grieve ruffed with the 6 and Hood overruffed with the 7. Declarer still had a certain trump loser, so he would have to set up the hearts in order to dispose of the losing club. He crossed to the ace of trumps and led a low heart, ruffing in the South hand. A diamond ruff returned the lead to dummy, leaving these cards still out:

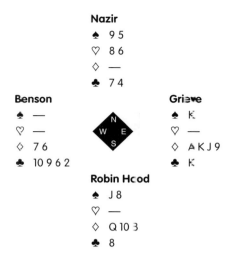

Nazir
♠ 9 5
♡ 8 6
◇ —
♣ 7 4

Benson
♠ —
♡ —
◇ 7 6
♣ 10 9 6 2

Grieve
♠ K
♡ —
◇ A K J 9
♣ K

Robin Hood
♠ J 8
♡ —
◇ Q 10 3
♣ 8

When Hood called for a good heart East ruffed with the king, hoping that declarer still had two clubs in his hand. It was not to be. Robin Hood discarded his last club and faced his remaining cards, claiming dummy's master heart and four trump tricks on a cross-ruff.

The final comparison revealed that the outlaw team had overcome the substantial half-time deficit and won the challenge match by 7 IMPs.

'Amazing how our luck turned like that,' declared Robin Hood as he took charge of the winning purse.

'It was the Devil's work,' snarled Benson. 'He moved the cards in your favour.'

'If that's true, I'm much obliged to him,' replied Hood. 'Quite a weight, this gold. I trust we will have a safe journey back to Nottingham.'

'You travellin' on the main road?' enquired Benson casually.

'Yes, first thing tomorrow morning,' replied Hood. 'We shall spend the night here.'

Benson and his team departed and the outlaws proceeded to celebrate their win with several jars of ale.

'You think the Nottingham road will be safe tomorrow, Robin?' said Little John, leaning forward to refill his glass. 'It's plagued by 'ighwaymen, so I've 'eard.'

Hood nodded. 'I fear that tomorrow a certain one-eyed highwayman may be waiting for us at some point,' he said.

'We could take the Matlock road instead,' suggested Friar Tuck. 'The journey is a little longer but I understand they make very fine pies in

Matlock.'

Nazir gazed out of the window, where a full moon lit the sky. 'Why not take the main road but set off now and ride through the night?' he suggested.

Robin Hood clapped the Saracen on the back. 'A much better idea,' he exclaimed. 'Yes, by the time our friend Benson opens his eye tomorrow, we'll be back in Nottingham!'

10
THE ST BONAVENTURE CHALICE

The Sheriff entered the barrack room and surveyed the dissolute scene. Gisburne and four fellow officers, tankards in hand, were playing dice.

'Gisburne!' cried the Sheriff. 'I take it that Robin Hood is safely under lock and key?'

'My Lord?' stammered Gisburne. 'What can you mean?'

'Since you see fit to while away the hours in idle pursuits,' continued the Sheriff, 'I assume that the prime duty assigned to you has been fulfilled.'

'Well, no, my Lord,' replied Gisburne. 'It is not for want of trying. Plan after plan has proved unsuccessful.'

'Perhaps I should spell it out to you, Gisburne,' said the Sheriff. 'If the man is not captured by the end of the month, I will have you replaced as commander of my guard. You will be reduced in rank to foot soldier.'

'But, my Lord,' protested Gisburne, 'the under-officers would make my life unbearable.'

The Sheriff headed towards the door. 'Quite so,' he replied. 'Perhaps that will sharpen your resolve.'

A few days later posters appeared all over Nottingham:

Be it knowne that on the Lord's Day, 25th June, a grande bridge payres tourney wylle be held in the Great Halle of Nottyngham. The first prize wylle be the St Bonaventure golden chalice, ruby-encrusted and of inestimable value. No entry fee wylle be charged.

'What think you of it?' asked Friar Tuck, as Robin Hood studied a copy of the poster. 'The smell of a trap could hardly be more obvious.'

'Such a piece of gold would feed the poor of Nottingham for many weeks,' replied Hood. 'Perhaps Nazir and I could disguise ourselves.'

'They will spot you immediately,' declared Tuck. 'Nazir cannot pass as an Englishman and few entrants will be as tall as you, disguised or not.'

'We could enter a decoy pair to distract attention from us,' suggested Robin Hood. 'Nathan the Poulterer is dark of complexion and his partner, William of Wykham, is of similar build to me. If they play in the event, crudely disguised, they will be taken for Nazir and me.'

'And what guise will you and Nazir take?' queried the Friar.

'I will think of something,' replied Robin Hood.

The great day soon arrived. Some one hundred and ten pairs had entered the event, attracted by the grand first prize. A new method of scoring would be used, whereby in each round pairs would play eight consecutive hands against a pair with a current score similar to their own.

Gisburne arrived to take his seat opposite the Sheriff. 'My plan could not have worked better, my Lord,' he declared excitedly. 'The two outlaws have been spotted already. Their first-round assignment has them on Table 32.'

'Don't try to take them now,' declared the Sheriff. 'They will be on their guard and the crowd might assist them to escape.'

'Very good, my Lord,' replied Gisburne. 'I will have my men arrest them at the end of the event, as they prepare to leave.'

Meanwhile, the real Robin Hood and Nazir faced two ladies of the court at Table 17. Hood had shaved off his legendary moustache and the pair had rubbed wood ash into their hair, aging their appearance by some 15 years. They wore the garb of pig farmers.

Love All. Dealer South.

	♠ A 4 2	
	♡ J 7 6 5 3	
	◇ J 8 4 3	
	♣ 8	
♠ Q 10 8		♠ 9 5
♡ Q 10 9 2		♡ 4
◇ A K Q 6		◇ 10 5 2
♣ Q 7		♣ J 10 9 6 5 4 2
	♠ K J 7 6 3	
	♡ A K 8	
	◇ 9 7	
	♣ A K 3	

West	North	East	South
Madame	Nazir	Hélène	Robin
Gorette		de The	Hood
			1♣
Dble	Rdble	Pass	1♠
1NT	2♠	Pass	4♠
All Pass			

When Robin Hood opened with a strong Nottingham Club, the elegantly attired Emilie Gonette eyed him disdainfully. *'Je contre,'* she said.

Nazir turned to his left. 'The double of a strong club means what?' he enquired.

As if by a feat of ventriloquism, the answer came from his right. 'It is for take-out of ze clubs,' replied Madame Gonette. 'Opening bid strength.'

Nazir redoubled, indicating a semi-positive of around 5-7 points.

'Je suis contente,' declared Hélène de Trouville, nodding happily.

Robin Hood rebid One Spade and soon arrived in Four Spades. Madame Gonette led the ace of diamonds and switched to the queen of clubs, won by declarer's ace. Two tricks would be lost in diamonds, so Hood could afford only one loser in the majors, despite West's take-out double which had suggested length there. He nodded to himself. Unless the redoubtable Madame Gonette held A-K-Q bare in diamonds, allowing him to establish a trick for dummy's jack, he would have to catch her in an endplay.

Robin Hood led a second round of diamonds, won by West's queen. He ruffed the club return in dummy and ruffed a diamond in his hand, failing to bring down the king. Both defenders followed to the king and ace of trumps. Hood ruffed dummy's last diamond and cashed the ace of hearts, leaving this end position:

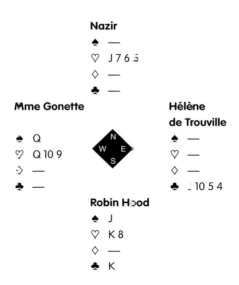

Nazir
♠ —
♡ J 7 6 5
♢ —
♣ —

Mme Gonette
♠ Q
♡ Q 10 9
♢ —
♣ —

Hélène de Trouville
♠ —
♡ —
♢ —
♣ 10 5 4

Robin Hood
♠ J
♡ K 8
♢ —
♣ K

When the king of clubs was led Madame Gonette considered the matter for a moment, then discarded a heart. The lay-out of the cards had been made obvious by West's original take-out double. Hood led the jack of trumps next, throwing West on lead. He called for dummy's jack on the enforced heart return and claimed the contract when East showed out.

'*Dix levées!*' exclaimed Madame de Gonette. '*Je ne peux pas le croire.*'

Hélène de Trouville gazed curiously at Robin Hood. '*Il est malodorant comme un Anglais,*' she observed, '*mais il joue les cartes comme un vrai Français.*'

As luck would have it, the pair impersonating Hood and Nazir won their first match 20–0. They were assigned to Table 1 for the second round and were alarmed to see Gisburne and the Sheriff awaiting them there.

'Remember who we're meant to be,' said William of Wykham. 'And be subtle about it, for Heaven's sake.'

The villagers took their seats. 'Ah, and who have we here?' said the Sheriff, peering intently at the men he took to be Robin Hood and Nazir.

'Er ... I be Sam the Wheelmaker,' replied William of Wykham.

'Yes, and I be Richard the Fruitpicker,' said his partner. 'Allah be praised.'

The Sheriff's eyes blazed for a moment, then he managed to control himself. 'Sam and Richard, then,' he said. 'Two worthy opponents for us, partner.'

Gisburne was staring at the opponents as though they were venomous snakes. 'So it seems, my Lord,' he said.

North/South Game. Dealer West.

```
                  ♠  K 3
                  ♡  A Q J 7 6 3
                  ◇  9 7 3
                  ♣  8 5
   ♠  8 5                          ♠  Q 10 9 2
   ♡  9 4          N               ♡  10 5 2
   ◇  8 4       W     E            ◇  Q J 10 2
   ♣  A Q J 10 7 6 2  S            ♣  9 4
                  ♠  A J 7 6 4
                  ♡  K 8
                  ◇  A K 6 5
                  ♣  K 3
```

West	North	East	South
William of	Guy of	Nathan	The
Wykham	Gisburne		Sheriff
3♣	3♡	Pass	4NT
Pass	5◇	Pass	6NT
All Pass			

William of Wykham made the passive lead of ♡9 against 6NT and Gisburne displayed his dummy somewhat nervously. 'I have only 10 points, my Lord,' he declared, 'but with six fine hearts I thought ....'

'Why do you bleat like a lamb every time you mis-bid?' demanded the Sheriff. 'It's bad enough having you play like a sheep. You don't need to sound like one as well.'

'My Lord,' complained Gisburne. 'In front of these er ... commoners, it's really too much.'

'Play small,' commanded the Sheriff, winning the trick with the king of hearts.

There were only ten top tricks and it seemed to the Sheriff that he would need to find East with three spades to the queen. Still, no damage could be done by running the heart suit first.

Nathan the Poulterer, sitting East, had to find three discards on the hearts. He could afford only one diamond discard and needed to keep all his spades. This was the position when the last heart was led:

Gisburne
- ♠ K 3
- ♡ 6
- ♢ 9 7 3
- ♣ 8 5

William
- ♠ 8 5
- ♡ —
- ♢ 8 4
- ♣ A Q J 10

Nathan
- ♠ Q 10 9 2
- ♡ —
- ♢ Q J 10
- ♣ 9

Sheriff
- ♠ A J 7 5 4
- ♡ —
- ♢ A K 6
- ♣ —

Nathan eventually decided to throw his last club. The Sheriff discarded ♢6 from his hand, cashed dummy's king of spades and played a spade to the jack. The finesse succeeded but when he continued with the spade ace West showed out. The Sheriff now exited with a spade, setting up a long card in the suit. East had to return a diamond and the Sheriff tossed his remaining cards on the table, triumphantly claiming the remainder.

'You see how my Three Heart call contributed?' said Gisburne. 'Only 10 high-card points but the playing strength was there.'

'It was my own "playing strength" that landed the twelve tricks,' retorted the Sheriff. 'No-one else in the shire would have come close.'

William of Wykham was staring open-mouthed at his partner. 'Keep a club and 'e goes a mile down,' he cried. 'I 'ad the ace-queen-jack of clubs sitting over 'is king.'

The Sheriff directed a scornful glance at the man he believed to be his great adversary. King of the murdering scum in Sherwood he might be but the man couldn't even recognise a simple squeeze.

The Sheriff and Gisburne eventually won the match by the handsome victory-point margin of 17 to 3.

'What pathetic creatures those outlaws are,' said the Sheriff to Gisburne. 'They risk their necks coming here in the feeblest of disguises and they won't come within a mile of winning the Chalice anyway.'

Meanwhile, down on Table 8, the real Robin Hood and Nazir were about to play their next match against two visiting money-lenders from Birmingham. Hood gathered his concentration. Nothing short of a 20-0 result would suffice if they were to close the gap on Gisburne and the Sheriff.

This was an early board in the match:

North/South Game. Dealer South.

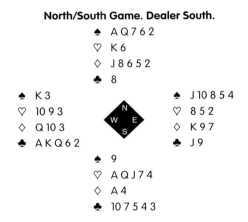

♠ A Q 7 6 2
♡ K 6
◇ J 8 6 5 2
♣ 8

♠ K 3
♡ 10 9 3
◇ Q 10 3
♣ A K Q 6 2

♠ J 10 8 5 4
♡ 8 5 2
◇ K 9 7
♣ J 9

♠ 9
♡ A Q J 7 4
◇ A 4
♣ 10 7 5 4 3

West	North	East	South
Eli	*Nazir*	*Jonathan*	*Robin*
Rosberg		*LeGrand*	
			1♡
2♣	2♠	Pass	3♡
Pass	4♡	All Pass	

West's overcall forced the outlaws' bidding up one level and it was unclear to Nazir how strong a hand Robin would hold for his rebid of Three Hearts. He decided to raise to Four Hearts and West led the ace of clubs. 'Small, please,' said Robin Hood.

At trick two the opulently dressed Rosberg switched to a small trump. Hood won with dummy's king, played a diamond to the ace, and took a successful spade finesse. He discarded his losing diamond on the spade ace and ruffed a diamond in the South hand. A club ruff in dummy brought down East's jack and Hood returned to the South hand by ruffing a diamond with the jack. The opponents' trumps fell conveniently under the ace and queen, leaving this end position:

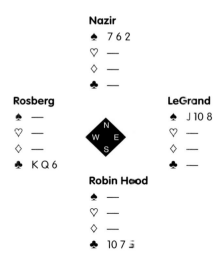

Nazir
- ♠ 7 6 2
- ♡ —
- ◇ —
- ♣ —

Rosberg
- ♠ —
- ♡ —
- ◇ —
- ♣ K Q 6

LeGrand
- ♠ J 10 8
- ♡ —
- ◇ —
- ♣ —

Robin Hood
- ♠ —
- ♡ —
- ◇ —
- ♣ 10 7 3

When Robin Hood exited with ♣10 Rosberg could not hide his annoyance. He scored two club tricks but had to surrender the game-going trick to declarer's ♣7.

'We bid it accurately,' said a delighted Nazir. 'Your club suit was just good enough.'

'Only opening lead to let it make,' complained the East player. 'Absolutely ridiculous, him making the seven of clubs like that.'

'Yes, stupid of me, so it was,' replied Rosberg, glaring at his partner. 'I don't know what came over me, so stupid it is to lead from ace-king-queen.'

The outlaw pair recorded a maximum win, causing them to jump to Table 2, just one table below the Sheriff. Their opponents in the penultimate round of the event would be Baron Morecambe and one of the wealthiest men in the shire, Sir Hugo Latham.

This was the big hand of the round.

North/South Game. Dealer South.

```
              ♠ 6 5 3 2
              ♡ A 6 3
              ◇ J 4 2
              ♣ K 10 5
   ♠ 8 4                      ♠ J 9
   ♡ Q J 10 4        N        ♡ K 9 8 5 2
   ◇ K 10 8 6    W     E      ◇ 9 5
   ♣ Q 7 3          S         ♣ 9 8 6 2
              ♠ A K Q 10 7
              ♡ 7
              ◇ A Q 7 3
              ♣ A J 4
```

West	North	East	South
Baron	*Nazir*	*Sir Hugo*	*Robin*
Morecambe		*Latham*	*Hood*
			1♣
Pass	1NT	Pass	2♠
Pass	3♠	Pass	4♣
Pass	4♡	Pass	6♠
All Pass			

The Baron was none too pleased at having to play against two unwashed peasants. Surely at this late stage of the event the top tables should be occupied solely by members of the landed gentry. He moved his chair back a foot or so, the better to escape the smell of pig's droppings, and led the queen of hearts against Six Spades. 'Play the ace,' said Robin Hood.

Foreseeing some sort of elimination ending, Hood ruffed a heart at trick 2. The enemy trumps were drawn in two rounds and Hood continued with a diamond towards the dummy. The Baron could not afford to go in with the king and the jack won the trick. Robin Hood took advantage of the entry to dummy by ruffing dummy's last heart. The lead was in the South hand and these cards remained:

Nazir
- ♠ 6 5
- ♡ —
- ♢ 4 2
- ♣ K 10 5

Baron
- ♠ —
- ♡ J
- ♢ K 10 8
- ♣ Q 7 3

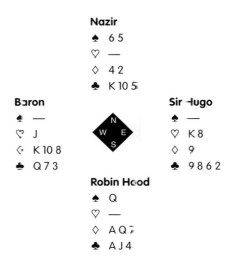

Sir Hugo
- ♠ —
- ♡ K 8
- ♢ 9
- ♣ 9 8 6 2

Robin Hood
- ♠ Q
- ♡ —
- ♢ A Q 7
- ♣ A J 4

Robin Hood's next play was ◊7. West covered with the 8 and East's 9 won the trick. Since a heart return would concede a ruff-and-discard, East had to open the clubs. Spared a guess in the suit, Robin Hood faced his cards. 'I make the rest now,' he said.

'You idiot, Hugo!' exclaimed the Baron. 'Unblock the 9 of diamonds on the first round and you cannot be endplayed.'

'You could have prevented it yourself,' replied Sir Hugo Latham. 'Put up the 10 of diamonds and you take my 9 under it.'

'All to no avail, I fear,' declared an amused Robin Hood. 'If West wins the second round of diamonds he is endplayed just the same.'

'You insolent serf!' cried Baron Morecambe. 'Your play gained absolutely nothing. You would have finessed me for the club queen anyway.'

'Quite so,' agreed Sir Hugo Latham. 'It is common knowledge that the queen lies over the jack more often than not.'

Just a few feet away, at table 1, the Sheriff and Gisburne were contesting their penultimate match. The opponents were two members of the court, Henri de Bourg and Léonard Brochard. Third to speak, at Love All, the Sheriff had just picked up this hand:

- ♠ Void
- ♡ A Q J 9 7 2
- ♢ A Q 8 4
- ♣ 8 7 3

The St Bonaventure Chalice

'One No-trump,' said Gisburne. This showed some 13-15 points.

'Four Spades,' said Henri de Bourg.

With any luck, thought the Sheriff, Gisburne would have nothing much wasted in spades. In that case his values would surely plug most of the gaps in his own hand. The magic king of hearts, king of diamonds, ace-king-queen of clubs would be enough for a grand. Still, no need to be greedy. 'Six Hearts,' said the Sheriff.

There was no further bidding and this proved to be the full deal:

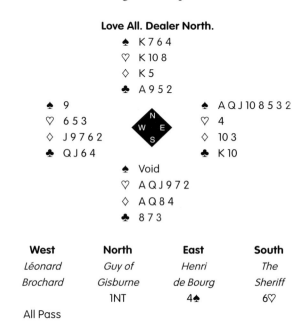

Love All. Dealer North.

	♠ K 7 6 4	
	♡ K 10 8	
	◇ K 5	
	♣ A 9 5 2	

♠ 9		♠ A Q J 10 8 5 3 2
♡ 6 5 3		♡ 4
◇ J 9 7 6 2		◇ 10 3
♣ Q J 6 4		♣ K 10

	♠ Void	
	♡ A Q J 9 7 2	
	◇ A Q 8 4	
	♣ 8 7 3	

West	North	East	South
Léonard	*Guy of*	*Henri*	*The*
Brochard	*Gisburne*	*de Bourg*	*Sheriff*
	1NT	4♠	6♡
All Pass			

West led ♠9 and down went the dummy. Typical of Gisburne to have a wasted king in the opponents' suit, thought the Sheriff. How on earth could he avoid two club losers? If trumps were 2-2 it might be possible to draw trumps, eliminate East's diamonds, then end play East with ace and another club. Still, Henri was a strong player. If he did hold a doubleton king of clubs he would surely unblock the king under dummy's ace.

The Sheriff could see a better line. At trick 2 he led a club, ducking the trick to East's 10. East's trump switch was won in the dummy and the Sheriff ruffed a spade high in his hand. A trump to the 10 permitted another high spade ruff. A club to dummy's ace dropped East's king, leaving this position:

Gisburne
- ♠ K
- ♡ K
- ◇ K 5
- ♣ 9 5

Brochard
- ♠ —
- ♡ 6
- ◇ J 9 7 6
- ♣ Q

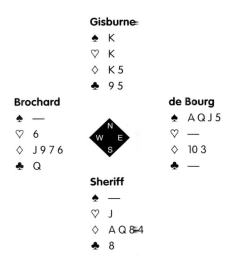

de Bourg
- ♠ A Q J 5
- ♡ —
- ◇ 10 3
- ♣ —

Sheriff
- ♠ —
- ♡ J
- ◇ A Q 8 4
- ♣ 8

'King of spades,' said the Sheriff. The king was covered by East's ace and ruffed with the jack of trumps. West now had no good card to play. To underruff would only delay matters; declarer would cross to the diamond king and squeeze him with the king of trumps. Brochard in fact threw a diamond. The Sheriff now crossed to dummy with a diamond and drew West's last trump, throwing a club from his hand. Three more diamond tricks followed and the slam had been made.

'Brilliant play, my Lord,' congratulated Gisburne. 'I had just the right cards for you.'

The board contributed handsomely to an 18-2 win. The Sheriff gazed contentedly at his scorecard. With a score of over 80% they must surely be uncatchable. It would be one of the most satisfying days of his life. Not only would it end with the villainous Robin Hood under lock and key, he would also remain in possession of an extremely valuable piece of church plate.

The event was not yet won, however. Unknown to the Sheriff, a pair of elderly pig farmers had also been doing well, collecting 20-0 scores in their last two matches.

'This is the big one,' whispered Robin Hood to Nazir, as they moved for their final match. 'The Sheriff awaits us!'

11
SHOOT-OUT AT TABLE ONE

'And who might you be?' said the Sheriff, gazing in disbelief at the two unkempt figures before him.

'Pig farmers from Worksop way, your Lordship,' replied Robin Hood.

'So I detect,' said the Sheriff, reaching for his smelling salts. 'You're filthy, both of you. You should never have been admitted to the event.'

Sir Guy of Gisburne nodded his agreement. 'Quite so, my Lord,' he said. 'I shall reprimand the guard at the gate.'

Robin Hood brushed some pig's droppings off his sleeve, in Gisburne's general direction, and proceeded to take his seat.

The Sheriff continued to glare at Hood. 'Is the custom of washing unheard of in Worksop?' he demanded.

'Many do wash,' replied Robin Hood. 'Never seen much point in it myself. Wouldn't keep clean long in our line of business.'

The hands for the last round were soon dealt. Play began and this was the first board:

North/South Game. Dealer South.

```
                    ♠ 9
                    ♡ A 9 7 6 2
                    ◇ A Q 3
                    ♣ Q 10 3 4
  ♠ K J 8 2                          ♠ Q 7 6 4 3
  ♡ Q 10 4         N                 ♡ K 8 3
  ◇ 10 8 7 5     W   E               ◇ K 9 4
  ♣ 6 5            S                 ♣ 7 2
                    ♠ A 10 5
                    ♡ J 5
                    ◇ J 6 2
                    ♣ A K 9 3
```

West	North	East	South
Robin	*The*	*Nazir*	*Guy of*
Hood	*Sheriff*		*Gisburne*
			1NT
Pass	3♡	Pass	3NT
All Pass			

Gisburne arrived in 3NT and Robin Hood led ♠2, Nazir's queen winning the trick. The ♠4 return was covered by the 10 and jack, Hood continuing with the king of spades to clear the suit.

Gisburne could count only eight top tricks and it seemed he would have to rely on a successful diamond finesse to bring the total to nine. Still, he thought, there was no hurry to take the critical finesse. If he ran the club suit first, one of these ignorant pig farmers might discard a spade winner.

On the third round of clubs Gisburne's wish came true. Robin Hood, sitting West, discarded ♠8. Gisburne cashed his two remaining clubs, forcing Nazir to find three discards in all. To bare the diamond king would have allowed declarer to succeed by playing ace and another diamond (not caring if West, now out of spades, won with the diamond king). Concluding that it was less dangerous to bare the king of hearts, Nazir discarded two hearts and one diamond.

The diamond finesse could be delayed no longer, concluded Gisburne. He played a diamond to the queen, losing to East's king. Nazir cashed the 7 and 6 of spades and the game was one down.

Gisburne looked apprehensively across the table. 'It all depended on the diamond finesse, my Lord,' he said. 'Five Clubs would have been safer. Perhaps you might have ....'

'You buffoon!' cried the Sheriff, causing several heads to turn in his direction. 'Their spades were blocked. Take the diamond finesse at trick 4 and you make it.'

'Impossible to tell, my Lord,' stammered Gisburne. 'I thought if I ran the clubs they might have problems with their discards.'

'West led the 2 of spades, you imbecile,' continued the Sheriff. 'So, apart from the king, jack and 2, he was known to hold just one more card in the suit, the 8, 7 or 6.'

'I couldn't tell which, my Lord,' said Gisburne.

'There was a solid 1-in-3 chance of a blockage if an immediate diamond finesse failed,' persisted the Sheriff. 'Only a half-wit would go down in the contract.'

Honours were shared on the next two boards, then the two outlaws had their defence tested.

East/West Game. Dealer North.

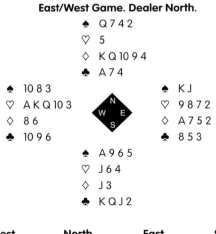

```
              ♠ Q 7 4 2
              ♡ 5
              ◇ K Q 10 9 4
              ♣ A 7 4
  ♠ 10 8 3                    ♠ K J
  ♡ A K Q 10 3        N       ♡ 9 8 7 2
  ◇ 8 6            W     E     ◇ A 7 5 2
  ♣ 10 9 6            S        ♣ 8 5 3
              ♠ A 9 6 5
              ♡ J 6 4
              ◇ J 3
              ♣ K Q J 2
```

West	North	East	South
Robin	The	Nazir	Guy of
Hood	Sheriff		Gisburne
	1◇	Pass	1♠
Pass	2♠	Pass	4♠
Pass			
All Pass			

Robin Hood led the ace of hearts against Four Spades, drawing the 5, 9 and 4. It seemed natural to switch to a club, hoping to set up a trick or two there before the diamonds could provide discards. However, in trump contracts Robin and Nazir had a special agreement whenever dummy held a singleton in the suit led. Their practice was to make a suit preference signal, to assist partner with his switch. Nazir would scarcely have signalled with the 9 of hearts if he held something good in clubs, so at trick two Robin Hood switched to ◇8. Nazir won with the ace and returned a second round of the suit, won in the South hand.

With two aces already conceded, Gisburne now had to lose only one trump trick. He was familiar with his holdings in the suit. Correct play was to start with the ace. If that drew the jack or 10 from East, then the next round should be ducked, hoping to find East with the bare king. The play had odds of 2-to-1 in its favour; it would gain against K-J or K-10 doubleton and lose only to J-10 doubleton.

Aware that the Sheriff was watching him closely, Gisburne cashed the ace of trumps. Yes, the jack came from East! He continued with a second round of trumps. West, who had played the 8 on the first round, now followed with the 3. 'Play low, my Lord,' said Gisburne.

Sir Guy of Gisburne's delight at the appearance of the king from East was short-lived. Nazir returned a third round of diamonds and West ruffed with the 10 of trumps. The contract was one down.

'I made a fine play in the trump suit, my Lord,' declared Gisburne. 'Unfortunately it was to no avail after that diamond switch.'

The Sheriff completed the score-sheet with a few angry strokes of his quill. How could a couple of moronic pig farmers from Worksop be proving so troublesome?

The Sheriff turned to address Robin Hood. 'What score were you on before this round started?' he demanded.

Hood inspected his assignment card. 'Er ... it says here that our score be 127, my Lord,' he replied.

'Good God!' exclaimed the Sheriff. 'That's only 13 fewer than us. Wake your ideas up, Gisburne.'

This was the next board:

Game All. Dealer East.

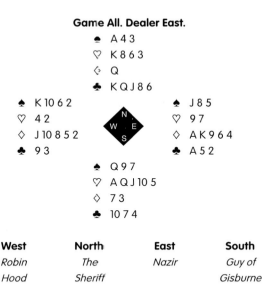

```
                     ♠ A 4 3
                     ♡ K 8 6 3
                     ◇ Q
                     ♣ K Q J 8 6
   ♠ K 10 6 2                      ♠ J 8 5
   ♡ 4 2                           ♡ 9 7
   ◇ J 10 8 5 2                    ◇ A K 9 6 4
   ♣ 9 3                           ♣ A 5 2
                     ♠ Q 9 7
                     ♡ A Q J 10 5
                     ◇ 7 3
                     ♣ 10 7 4
```

West	North	East	South
Robin	*The*	*Nazir*	*Guy of*
Hood	*Sheriff*		*Gisburne*
		1◇	1♡
Pass	4♡	All Pass	

Robin Hood saw little point in supporting the diamonds at his first turn. The hand was likely to belong to the opponents and by raising the diamonds he would merely assist them to judge their degree of fit.

Hood's lead of the jack of diamonds was covered by the queen and king. The critical moment of the hand had already arrived. It was obvious to Nazir that declarer would soon be able to set up the club suit. Before that was done, the defenders would need to establish two spade tricks. At trick two, Nazir switched to a carefully chosen card – the jack of spades.

Gisburne covered with the spade queen, drawing the king and ace. Trumps were drawn in two rounds and Gisburne then led a club to the king. Nazir took the ace immediately and returned an impassive ♠5.

Time stood still as Gisburne surveyed his remaining 9 and 7 in the spade suit, uncertain which card to play. If East had started with just ♠J-5, his play would make no difference. If East had started with ♠J-10-5, it was essential to rise with the 9. Still, playing pairs and with discards on the club suit imminent, surely the pig farmer would have made certain of cashing his 10. Against that, how could playing the 7 gain? Only if East had found an obscure jack from J-8-5. Who in his right mind would do that?

Gisburne eventually tossed the ♠9 on to the table. Hood won with the 10 and returned a spade to Nazir's 8. The game was one down.

'How can it be right to play the nine of spades?' demanded the Sheriff. 'If East held the 10 he would have cashed it. Do you think he hadn't noticed the club suit was good for discards?'

'The jack on the first round made it difficult for me, my Lord,' said Gisburne. 'I should have thought that __'

'Yes, you should have thought,' retorted the Sheriff. He looked down at his personal scorecard. How could they possibly be doing so badly against this imbecilic opposition?

The Sheriff and Gisburne fared well on two part-score deals. The players then drew their cards for the final hand of the event.

East/West Game. Dealer North.

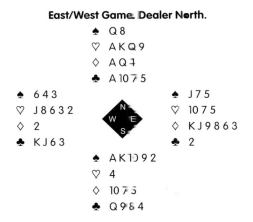

```
                    ♠ Q 8
                    ♡ A K Q 9
                    ◇ A Q 4
                    ♣ A 10 7 5
    ♠ 6 4 3                         ♠ J 7 5
    ♡ J 8 6 3 2                     ♡ 10 7 5
    ◇ 2                             ◇ K J 9 8 6 3
    ♣ K J 6 3                       ♣ 2
                    ♠ A K 10 9 2
                    ♡ 4
                    ◇ 10 7 5
                    ♣ Q 9 8 4
```

West	North	East	South
Robin	*The*	*Nazir*	*Guy of*
Hood	*Sheriff*		*Gisburne*
	2NT	Pass	3♠
Pass	3NT	Pass	4♣
Pass	4◇	Pass	4♠
Pass	6♣	All Pass	

Robin Hood led his singleton ◇2 against the slam and down went the dummy. Gisburne eyed the West player suspiciously. Since he was leading through the strong hand it was entirely possible that the lead was from the king. Still, little would be gained by a successful finesse; the diamond losers in his hand could be discarded anyway.

'Don't take all day over it,' grunted the Sheriff. 'Remember that you will soon have an important duty to perform.'

'A dozen of my men are watching their table, my Lord,' replied Gisburne. 'No escape is possible.'

Gisburne rose with dummy's ace of diamonds and successfully cashed three rounds of hearts, discarding his remaining diamonds. He then called for a small trump. East played the 2 and Gisburne finessed the 9. With no apparent thought Robin Hood won the trick with the king. A low spade switch went to the jack and ace, Gisburne continuing confidently with a trump to the ace. His mouth fell open when East showed out on the trick. 'You have no more trumps?' he gasped.

Nazir shook his head and Gisburne conceded one down.

'How can you be fooled by a mere pig farmer?' cried the Sheriff. 'Win the spade switch with the queen, for Heaven's sake. Then you can lead a low trump from dummy on the second round, intending to finesse the 8.'

'Does that make any difference, my Lord?' queried a flustered Gisburne.

'Of course it does, you idiot,' continued the Sheriff. 'When East shows out, you can win with the queen and pick up the trumps.'

Play had finished at many of the tables and some pairs were beginning to leave the Great Hall. Suddenly a dozen men-at-arms swarmed round table 23 in the Red section. The East-West players were manhandled to the floor, bound hand and foot, and carried to the Castle keep.

'Good gracious!' exclaimed Hélène de Trouville, who was standing nearby. 'Zey were playing some convention zat is not allowed?'

'No, no, my dear,' replied her partner. 'I heard someone say it is ze famous outlaw Robin Hood and one of his men.'

The Sheriff and Gisburne strode at high speed towards the keep. 'No mistakes this time, my Lord,' declared Gisburne, as the dungeon door was unlocked for them. 'Hood and the Saracen are in irons and attended by no fewer than six guards.'

'At last!' cried the Sheriff, gazing triumphantly at the two figures cowering in a corner. 'Now let me make sure I get your name right,' he said, addressing the taller of the two men. 'You are called Sam, are you not?'

'That be right, my Lord,' came the reply. 'Sam the Wheelmaker.'

'Ah yes, a wheelmaker,' said the Sheriff. 'I have one small question for you. Do you have an arrow scar on your right shoulder-blade?'

'No, my Lord.'

'Ah no, of course,' said the Sheriff heavily. 'My mistake. For a moment I was confusing you with Robin Hood, the outlaw leader. By common knowledge he does have such a scar.'

'Strip him!' cried Gisburne.

The Sheriff and Gisburne inspected the man's back in disbelief. Search as they might, no arrow scar could be found. A dreadful moment of realisation struck the Sheriff. 'The pig farmers!' he cried. 'Back to the Great Hall!'

The tables were being cleared away in the Great Hall and few people remained. 'Where is everyone?' demanded the Sheriff.

'Gone 'ome, I s'pose,' replied a captain of the guard. 'The pair from Worksop won it. Scored 20-0 in their last match, apparently.'

'They have the St Bonaventure Chalice?' gasped the Sheriff.

'I believe so,' replied the captain. 'Left in quite a hurry, they did. Had horses brought round for them.'

The Sheriff directed a murderous glance in Gisburne's direction, then turned once more to the captain. 'Did they, by any tiny chance, happen to ride off in the direction of Sherwood?'

'Right as always, my Lord, and very fine riders they were,' replied the captain. 'For pig farmers, anyway.'

To my sister Ann
RI

To James
MK

Rose Impey has become one of Britain's most prominent children's story tellers. She used to be a primary teacher and still spends much of her time in schools reading her work to children.

Moira Kemp is a highly respected illustrator. When illustrating the 'Creepies' she drew heavily from her own childhood experience.

First published in 2004
by Mathew Price Ltd
The Old Glove Factory
Bristol Road, Sherborne
Dorset DT9 4HP

Designed by Douglas Martin
Produced by Mathew Price Ltd
Printed in Singapore

The Flying Vampire

Rose Impey
Illustrated by Moira Kemp

Mathew Price Limited

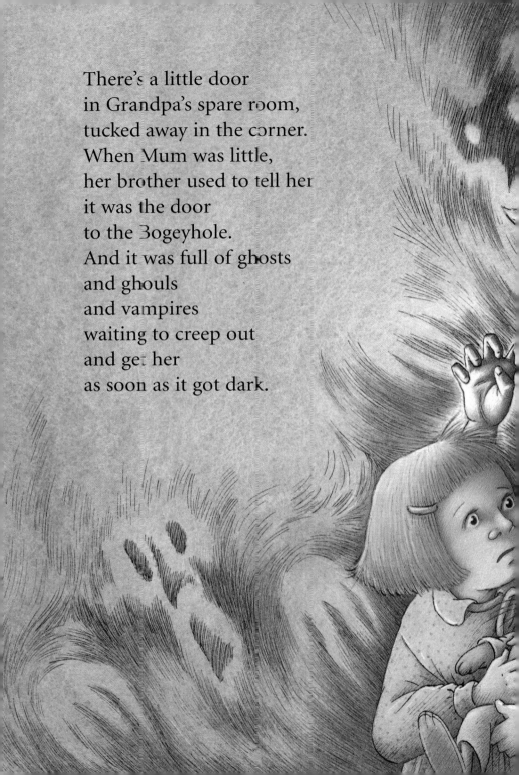

There's a little door
in Grandpa's spare room,
tucked away in the corner.
When Mum was little,
her brother used to tell her
it was the door
to the Bogeyhole.
And it was full of ghosts
and ghouls
and vampires
waiting to creep out
and get her
as soon as it got dark.

He was only kidding;
trying to scare her.
He's like that, my uncle Roo.
But now, when I go to stay with Grandpa,
I have to sleep in that room,
the room with the Bogeyhole.

I'm not really scared;
I know it was only a joke.
But before I get into bed
I ask Grandpa to show me,
just to be sure.
"There you are," he says.
"Just a lot of old junk.
Nothing to be afraid of."

I peer inside, but all I can see
are big dark shapes
and spooky-looking shadows.

And I wish Grandpa would
close the door, quickly,
before any of them get out.

Hidden behind the door
is a big kite shaped like a dragon.
"I'd forgotten all about this," says Grandpa.

And he takes it out and hangs it
on the wall right over my bed.
"If you go straight to sleep," he says,
we'll fly this tomorrow."

But how can I go to sleep
when I'm lying here,
on my own in the dark,
thinking about all those shapes and
shadows in the Bogeyhole?

And how can I close my eyes
when I need to keep them wide open
and fixed on that door,
just in case?

I sit up in bed and call down,
"Grandpa! Can I have a light on?
I don't feel very well."

Grandpa comes up
and finds me a nightlight.
He sits on my bed, stroking my head,
telling me jokes.

So I'm okay now.
I know there's nothing to be afraid of.
There are no such things as ghosts
and ghouls
and vampires.
It was only Uncle Rob's joke.

And I turn over onto my side
and watch the nightlight flickering,
casting shadows round the room.
Long thin spiky ones
and little soft blobby ones.

There's one that looks like a big dragon.
It's the kite Grandpa hung
on the bedroom wall.
The kite that came out of the Bogeyhole.
But now it looks like a *flying vampire*.
. . . and its starting to move.

I'm not really scared.
I know it's only the flame from the nightlight;
the hot air rising makes the kite flutter.
But it looks as if its wings
are gently rising and falling,
rising and falling,
as if it's about to take flight.

Whoosh! suddenly its whole body rises up
and flaps as if it's coming to life.
I try not to panic.
I know it's only a kite.
But it did come out of the Bogeyhole.
And then I start to think
perhaps it really *is* a Flying Vampire
just pretending to be a kite.

I lie there holding my breath,
watching it.
But how can I watch it
and keep my eye on the door?

Because I'm starting to wonder
what else could come
creeping out of the Bogeyhole
now that my back is turned.

I roll over quickly, so I can watch the door.
But *now* I can't keep my eye on
The Flying Vampire!
Any moment it could really start to fly.

I picture it, gliding silently through the air,
trailing its shadow across the ceiling,
around the walls, circling the room,
swooping and soaring.

I can feel its sharp beady eyes
fixed on me right now;
its mouth wide open;
its fangs ready to sink into me.

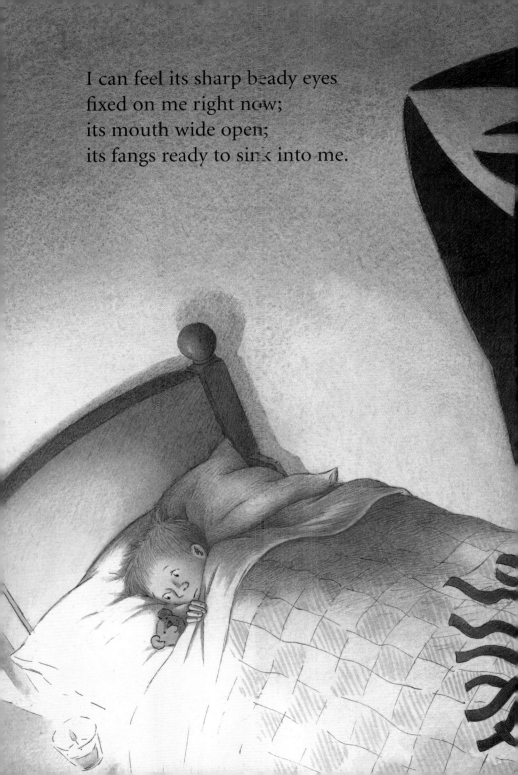

I duck down under the covers,
and pretend I'm in a tent.
I squeeze my eyes shut.
But I can still picture
The Flying Vampire
hovering over my bed,
preparing to pounce.

Here it comes! Diving Down!
Its claws stretched out;
its wings beating so fast
I can almost hear them.

But I'm ready for it.
I know what to do with vampires.
I throw off the covers
"Keep back!" I say.

Then I grab my pillow,
swinging it round and round,
beating it off.

The Flying Vampire flies up in the air.
It races across the room,
crash-landing on the carpet
right in front of the door,
the door to the Bogeyhole.

I climb out of bed,
keeping my eyes fixed on it,
and creep across the carpet.

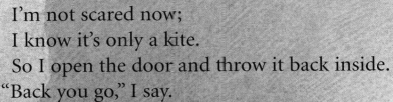

I'm not scared now;
I know it's only a kite.
So I open the door and throw it back inside.
"Back you go," I say.
"Back to the Bogeyhole."

But I close the door with a loud SLAM!
– just in case.